Architectural Crafts

The Western States Arts Foundation

The Western States Arts Foundation is a regional alliance of the state arts agencies of Arizona, Colorado, Idaho, Montana, Nevada, New Mexico, Oregon, Utah, Washington, and Wyoming. The member states formed the Foundation in 1974 to extend the reach of their individual resources in serving artists and advancing the arts in the West.

The regional approach to problem-solving is particularly useful in the West because these ten states share many common characteristics such as vast areas, sparse populations, and limited financial resources.

The Foundation fulfills its function by providing programs and services that can be planned, supported, and implemented more effectively by a regional non-profit organization than by individual state agencies.

For more information about the crafts-in-architecture project or other regional arts activities, contact Western States Arts Foundation, 141 East Palace Avenue, Santa Fe, New Mexico 87501; phone: (505) 988-1166.

The state arts agencies are the best source of information about arts programs, services, and activities in each state. Contact the appropriate agency for more details.

Arizona Commission on the Arts and
  Humanities
2024 North Seventh Street, Suite 201
Phoenix, Arizona 85006
(602) 255-5882

Idaho Commission on the Arts
C/o Statehouse Mail
Boise, Idaho 83720
(208) 334-2119

Nevada State Council on the Arts
329 Flint Street
Reno, Nevada 89501
(702) 784-6231

Oregon Arts Commission
835 Summer Street
Salem, Oregon 97301
(503) 378-3625

Washington State Arts Commission
Ninth and Columbia Building
Mail Stop GH-11
Olympia, Washington 98504
(206) 753-3860

Colorado Council on the Arts and
  Humanities
770 Pennsylvania Street
Denver, Colorado 80203
(303) 866-2617

Montana Arts Council
1280 South Third Street West
Missoula, Montana 59801
(406) 543-8286

New Mexico Arts Division
113 Lincoln Avenue
Santa Fe, New Mexico 87501
(505) 827-2061

Utah Arts Council
617 East South Temple Street
Salt Lake City, Utah 84102
(801) 533-5895

Wyoming Council on the Arts
Capitol Complex
Cheyenne, Wyoming 82202
(307) 777-7742

ARCHITECTURAL CRAFTS

a handbook and a catalog

BRIDGET BEATTIE McCARTHY

In conjunction with the Western States Arts Foundation

Madrona Publishers   Seattle   1982

FIRST EDITION
10 9 8 7 6 5 4 3 2 1

Library of Congress Cataloging in Publication Data

McCarthy, Bridget Beattie.
  Architectural crafts.

  Includes index.
  1. Decoration and ornament, Architectural — United
States.   2. Art industries and trade — United States
— History — 20th century.   3. Interior decoration —
United States — History — 20th century.   I. Title.
NA3504.M35   729   81-23649
ISBN 0-914842-80-3   AACR2

Published by
Madrona Publishers, Inc.
2116 Western Avenue
Seattle, Washington 98121

Cover: Clerestory window by Ed Carpenter
Cover photo by Karlis Grants

Book and cover design by Cynthia Bell

This publication was supported in part by a grant from the
National Endowment for the Arts.

Many of the craftsmen in this book are women; the terms
craftsman and *craftsmen* as used here are general terms that
apply to either sex.

Acknowledgments

I would like to thank the following people for sharing their
experiences, expertise, and vision, without which this book
would not have been possible: Dick Spies, Mirza Dickel,
Eudorah Moore, M. C. McCarthy, Ed Carpenter, Martha
West, Bill Bachuber, Peter Hero, Jon Schleuning, the staff of
the Fountain Gallery, John Frohnmayer, Sande Percival,
Michael Scott, Leonard DuBoff, Jacquelyn Kitzelman, Jerry
Yoshitomi, Carl Petrick, Cheryl Alters, Bill Jamison, and the
staff of Madrona Publishers. In addition, I would like to
thank the many people and organizations who provided
photographs to illustrate particular points in both the
handbook and the catalog.

Preface

The Western States Arts Foundation is publishing this book to recognize and encourage a significant recent development in the fields of crafts and architecture. In a revival of practices that died out gradually after the Industrial Revolution, there is today renewed interest in working partnerships between architects and craftsmen. In the past it was common for craftsmen to design ironwork, cabinetry, hardware, and other decorative architectural details in collaboration with architects and builders, but the availability of mass-produced materials undermined that connection about a century ago.

In recent years a growing number of architects and craftsmen have become interested in reviving their traditional collaboration. In architecture there have been renewed concerns about livability and the psychological impact of space; many designers today are more interested in warmth and uniqueness in an environment than in the austerity of form and function. To achieve this warmth and individuality, more and more architects have been going to craftsmen for hand-carved woodwork, stained-glass panels, ceramic murals, and other craftwork that can be integrated into the design of their structures. Craftsmen have responded eagerly, seeing new opportunities for their talents in working on an architectural scale.

The results of this renewed collaboration can be impressive, but the process of working together has not always been smooth. Architects sometimes have initial difficulties identifying and locating appropriate craftsmen. If that is not a problem, a clash of artistic wills can be. Craftsmen normally design and create on their own, and although architects are frequently more used to working in collaboration, they are accustomed to being in charge. There are different needs, languages, and priorities to be understood.

This book is intended to help address these problems and to indicate the creative potential that lies beyond them. It identifies over a hundred craftsmen with experience in architectural work and discusses the ramifications of artistic collaboration. We hope that *Architectural Crafts* will encourage more architects, interior designers, contractors, and clients to consider the use of craftwork integrated into architecture.

The book is divided into two sections. The text gives a historical perspective on architecturally integrated crafts, and deals with the complex issues of working together. It suggests some solutions to potential problems but is meant primarily to give a concise overview of the issues. Included also are examples of successful collaborations in the Western states.

The catalog section is comprised of work from 108 craftsmen who live in the ten states served by the Foundation: Arizona, Colorado, Idaho, Montana, Nevada, New Mexico, Oregon, Utah, Washington, and Wyoming. These people were selected from several hundred entrants by a jury composed of architect Cab Childress, interior designer Mirza Dickel, craft gallery owner Jo Ann Rapp, and architectural crafts consultant Bridget Beattie McCarthy.

Entry criteria restricted the competition to craftsmen who had done at least three pieces that had been successfully integrated or clearly could be integrated. A window commissioned for a particular building, wrought iron hardware that would have a number of applications, production ceramic sinks, and rugs produced on speculation were equally eligible. Selection was based on quality of design and workmanship, and also on the aesthetic and practical appropriateness of the work to its environment — was it, or could it be, truly integrated? Jurors were allowed to choose as many entrants for inclusion in the catalog as they felt were worthy.

Although the catalog showcases a wide variety of work, it is not a total cross-section of Western architectural crafts. Some talented craftsmen may not have heard about the competition despite a large publicity effort, and others could not put together the extensive entry materials before the deadline or had made a career decision to avoid competitions. But certainly the craftsmen featured in the catalog are a good place to begin a search for the unique and handcrafted. They have already exhibited a talent for working with architects, interior designers, and clients; they know how to help make spaces that represent the creativity of all while standing as complete entities. Their selection for the catalogue is a recognition of their talent and their established success in collaborative efforts.

Numerous people contributed to this project in essential ways. Bridget McCarthy, who authored the text, organized the catalog, served as a juror, and over the past year and a half, has provided her expertise, guidance, and unfailing enthusiasm every step of the way. The other jurors — Cab Childress, Mirza Dickel, and JoAnn Rapp — also deserve thanks for persevering through several of the longest, most difficult, and thought-provoking days of selection ever witnessed. Dan and Sara Levant, along with the rest of the staff at Madrona Publishers, appreciated the importance and timeliness of the subject and, from the project's inception, have worked diligently to bring this book to completion. The many craftsmen who took the time to assemble and submit slides, photographs, biographies, and related materials provided confirmation of the catalog's need. The Foundation is grateful to all who competed in the jury process. Other craftsmen, architects, interior designers, editors, and attorneys have contributed valuable and appreciated advice.

The Foundation's Board of Directors, made up of the director and chair of each of the ten state arts agencies, deserves much recognition for envisioning, initiating, and supporting the project. Staff members from each state agency were of great help in locating craftsmen and in promoting first the competition and now this publication. All Foundation staff members provided support and assistance, but Midge Cavin, Patty Nelson, and MarySue Sharp deserve special thanks for their help in cataloging entries and slides, supporting the jury process, and fielding a barrage of telephone calls from curious craftsmen. And the in-house legal expertise of Joseph K. Daly was essential.

The Foundation is grateful to the National Endowment for the Arts for the financial assistance given this book and to the Design Committee of the American Institute of Architects for its special interest in collaborations between artists and architects.

Cheryl Alters
Director of Special Projects

Bill Jamison
Executive Director
Western States Arts Foundation

Architectural Crafts

Contents

Architectural Crafts: An Historical Perspective

Crafts have long been integrated into architectural settings in the form of architectural detailing, sculpture, and custom-designed furniture and accessories. In the past, the term *craftsman* in the architectural sense has referred for the most part to the plasterer or blacksmith or seamstress who executed the architect's or interior designer's ideas in whatever medium was appropriate.

Ironwork, cornice detailing, railing design, and cabinetry were usually drawn up as part of the architect's working drawings and submitted first to the client for approval and then to the contractor or craftsmen for execution. Built-in shelving, gates, stone masonry, hardware, tilework, and other elements of functional and ornamental detail were (and sometimes still are) included as part of the total package and reflected the vision of the architect or interior designer.

While architects and interior designers are still designing much of the architectural detailing, the practice was far more prevalent before the Industrial Revolution, because far more craftsmen were available to carry out the work. Following the Industrial Revolution, many craftsmen went to work in factories because, as fewer people were able to afford to purchase work of the hand, the demand for the craftsmen's products diminished. Although, initially, factory-made items were intriguing, their appeal has gradually declined.

Since the Industrial Revolution, architects and interior designers have for the most part been restricted to mass-produced objects that, although often of good design, are limited in variety. Even the best catalogs offer only a few choices, in part because it is so costly for a factory to retool to change a design. Craftsmen, on the other hand, have the ability to design and execute such items as individualized bannisters, door hinges, tiles, sinks, and facades, and can work in materials that are different from those readily available to the trade.

Nevertheless, with the exception of such archi-

The Lloyd Frank estate in Portland, Oregon is an elegant example of an architect's devotion to detail. Here a concrete bird surveys the estate grounds from a perch at the corner of the house.

Exterior wall of the Lloyd Frank estate, showing several kinds of architectural craftwork. Herbert Brookman, who designed the estate, worked with craftsmen from all over the country and oversaw every detail of their work.

1

Detail of exterior wall on the Frank estate.

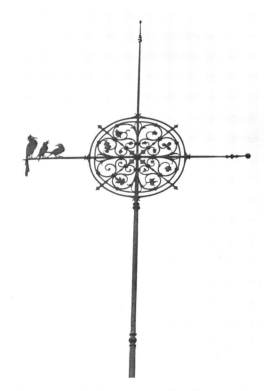

Metal weather vane on the Frank estate. The birds are the craftsman's—not nature's—creation.

Hand-wrought-iron wall sconce in the Lloyd Frank home. The estate was designed in the twenties.

Door hinge, Lloyd Frank estate.

tects as Frank Lloyd Wright, who designed the furniture for some of his buildings himself, decisions about unattached artwork and furnishings have usually been in the hands of the client, who commissions or purchases these items separately. Customarily, the architect has not become involved in this aspect of a building project.

Should a landscape architect or interior designer be involved, he or she has traditionally either purchased or had designed to his specifications those things he felt would enhance the areas with which he is concerned. Unfortunately, he is often introduced late in the project and is often frustrated by the apparent paucity of creative craftsmen with whom he can work. Bricklayers and steel fabricators are available, but craftsmen who can interpret a designer's ideas and contribute their special design and execution talents to the creation of truly unique solutions have been hard to come by. Thus, in the recent past it has been easier to order building accessories from a catalog.

Since the Industrial Revolution there have been a few attempts to revive that architect-craftsman relationship that existed in the past. The Arts and Crafts Movement spearheaded by William Morris in the late nineteenth century was a protest against machine-age artificiality. Short-lived revivals by the Bauhaus in Germany and the Works Progress Administration in the United States in the 1930s were attempts to integrate crafts into architecture

FRIENDS OF TIMBERLINE

Timberline Lodge, on Mount Hood in Oregon, is an outstanding example of the successful blending of crafts and architecture that took place during the WPA (Works Progress Administration) during the Depression.

Main entrance to Timberline Lodge. The lodge was built and furnished by craftsmen working under the guidance of interior designer Margery Hoffman Smith, who was involved in the overall design and saw to it that patterns and designs were repeated throughout the building, both in furnishings and in structural elements.

again in some kind of coherent and meaningful way.

Today the term *craftsman* has become confusing. In this country — with the exception of bricklayers, sheet-metal workers, and other craftsmen in the trades, those attached to a folk culture or geographically isolated group, and a few outstanding designer-craftsmen who never gave up — it was not until the late forties and fifties that we saw a widespread resurgence of the whole concept of the designer-craftsman. It was in this post-war period that university art departments began expanding to accommodate G.I. Bill beneficiaries of World War II. By the sixties a different kind of craftsman had begun to emerge alongside the bricklayers and metalworkers. This reborn designer-craftsman often took more pride and interest in his design than in its execution, promotion, or sale. Although he called himself a craftsman, the term became misleading since he was the product of a university art department with its emphasis on design and the

purity of the art form. The guilds and then the unions have taken care of many of the practical needs of craftsmen in the building trades, but the mechanics of being a practicing craftsman were rarely considered in university settings.

Meanwhile, those who were engaged in the alternative lifestyle of the sixties and the whole movement toward self-sufficiency, rejecting formal education and so-called stifling occupations, were drawn to the field of crafts as a means of financial support. While this group's purpose in life was ostensibly anticommercial, its interest in the production of crafts was to a large degree based purely on economics: sales without a middleman. Pots and jewelry and leather handbags were produced in quantities to be sold at ever-increasing numbers of crafts fairs.

By the late seventies, those craftsmen who had lived through the crafts fairs, as well as those who were university-trained and confronted with

The design of this dining-room chair at Timberline Lodge echoes the building's post and lintel architecture.

Iron door knocker at the main entrance to Timberline Lodge.

Desk and chair in writing alcove at Timberline Lodge. The unity of crafts and architecture throughout the lodge is the result of the willingness of each craftsman to work on parts of a design that was not his own.

Carved wooden bear head on the end of a structural beam at Timberline Lodge.

decreasing numbers of teaching opportunities, were ready to take another look at their chances for survival. The bricklayers, of course, had their unions, but both street-fair craftsmen and the designer-craftsmen began to realize that good business practices were essential to their existence.

A survey of the marketplace in the eighties reveals a public looking for the unique. We have all the mass-produced, modern conveniences that we can imagine. The sixties told us that we didn't want to be limited anymore, and that concept is now taking effect. What craftsmen have to offer today is the ability to add warmth and meaning to our society with the unique work of the hand. This reflects the material cultural heritage that we are seeking, now that our technologically efficient society has made it possible for us to jet around the world and view a space landing on the moon from our living-room TV sets. Architecturally integrated craftwork has the ability to leave lasting statements that can help future generations understand the culture of our times.

With the advent of the National Endowment for the Arts and the government percent-for-art programs of the seventies, sculpture, paintings, and murals began to appear again in bank lobbies,

BILL BACHUBER

Harold Balazs' gargoyle, with its own rain grate and downspout, is one of three executed in response to architect John Storr's desire for whimsy in what would otherwise have been an all too serious courtyard at the Oregon School of Arts and Crafts in Portland.

hotels, courtyards, and other public spaces. Simultaneously, corporations began acquiring their own art and craft collections, sometimes commissioning work directly.

Certainly, there is an eternal need for artists to express themselves freely, and for paintings and sculptures to be created independently from the environment in which they will be placed. However, there is an equally strong need for spaces to be conceived as whole entities, for which the talents of both artist or craftsman and architect are used to create an integrated environment that is pleasing and understandable even to the unsophisticated observer. Thus, art-in-public-places programs have really worked best when those involved in the design aspects of the project — architects and interior designers, who are artists in their own right, and artists and craftsmen — were all able to work together from the project's inception in an

COURTESY INTERNATIONAL PAPER CO.

The International Paper Company commissioned Lelooska and his family to carve native-American motifs for its Portland offices.

atmosphere where there was mutual respect as well as the opportunity for the give and take of ideas.

In the early eighties, the austere building design of the past thirty years began to undergo a change. The public's renewed interest in spaces that have personal meaning and, in addition, reflect a sense of regionalism, has created a climate in which architects and designers — as well as the public itself — have a genuine need for craftsmen to embellish buildings with ornamentation of a unique character to which people can relate.

In some respects, practicality is now being overshadowed by a need for the unique. Ten or fifteen years ago clients insisted on ease of main-tenance in materials, above all else; today they often accept warped Mexican tiles with chipped and upturned edges, because they are obviously handmade. Since high technology is readily avail-able to anybody who can afford it, individually designed and decorated surroundings are one of the ways businesses and individuals can set themselves apart from their neighbors or their competitors.

Interior designers and architects have had an increasingly difficult time finding the unique objects they needed to complement their buildings, particularly as the gap between designers and craftsmen widened as an effect of the technological society ushered in by the Industrial Revolution. Clients are now demanding individuality — but everything looks the same. Building-materials catalogs carry only mass-produced objects with certain finishes. Many architects and designers are interested in unusual finishes and custom-designed hardware, but they have trouble finding them. Moreover, they are not always confident that crafts-men can meet design criteria and schedules, or work efficiently with architects and others in the build-ing trade. Nevertheless, craftsmen are beginning to work with architects and designers and when these collaborations have been successful, they have sometimes been sensational. There have been a number of instances in which a craftsman's input

Ed Carpenter was commissioned to make two glass panels on either side of the entrance of the Adventist Hospital Chapel in *Portland. He suggested the incorporation of a hand-carved door by Lu Himes as part of the overall design shown here.*

Metalsmith J. Carl Freedman, when confronted with the structural problem of joining posts and beams for the framework of Sally and Bill Worcester's glass-blowing studio in Cannon Beach, Oregon, without hiding the detail of the joinery, came up with this ingenious system of beam support braces with forged mortise and tenon bolts.

contributed to an architectural solution in a most intriguing way.

The time has obviously come for a creative reunion of architect or interior designer and craftsman. While architects and craftsmen still must try to understand each other's needs and language — and both must always respect the limits of budget, technology, and clients' tastes — they are beginning to work together to produce results that represent the creativity of each while forming a unified whole. So far, only a few stellar examples have been created. However, as architects, interior designers, and craftsmen develop new respect for one another's values and perspectives, an exciting new panorama of possibilities is opening up.

Fireplace and ducting by the Architectural Sheetmetal Company of New River, Arizona. This company, a unique collaboration of David Platt, metal craftsman, and William Bruder, architect, provides finely designed and crafted metal objects to complement architectural environments. The design concepts are initiated by the architect and the details are refined by the metal craftsman.

Working with Craftsmen

The architects and interior designers who have been most successful at incorporating the work of craftsmen have, from the outset of a project, shared with the craftsmen their visions for a building or space. In addition, the architects or interior designers encouraged feedback about those areas where work could interact. Throughout each phase of design and construction, communication actively continued until the project was completed. These factors, however, are not always possible. Sometimes a project is not large enough to merit long-term and intricate planning; sometimes already produced work may be available to solve a problem. Or perhaps economy or weather dictate the substitution of the fast-track process for the conventional design process. Handmade hinges produced in limited quantities by a craftsman may make it unnecessary for an architect or interior designer to order custom-designed ones. Or the permafrost in Alaska may dictate construction of the first floor before completion of the design of an entire building.

All things being ideal, however, and since many architects think in terms of program, concepts, schematics, design development, construction-documents, and construction phases, the following might be a convenient way to think about including craftwork in a project.

Ask the client if he wants art or craft objects or detailing during the program phase, when the client first discusses with the architect or interior designer his interest in building or remodeling and when the function of the spaces is being outlined. It is at this time, as the basic goals, the quality level, and the overall look are discussed, that the whole issue of what craftsmen can contribute to the style and feeling of a space should be considered.

During this phase the ground rules should be outlined for all parties involved, including the craftsmen. The architect or interior designer and the client should determine a procedure for

selecting craftsmen and then review budgets and schedules to allow for the proper interaction of all team members. The amount of money to be spent on architectural detail and the budget arrangements for substituting handmade objects for commercial ones should both be discussed with the client at this time. (For instance, if a handmade sink is provided by a craftsman, the cost of the sink fixture usually charged by a plumbing subcontractor can often be deducted from that part of the construction budget.)

Often craftsmen are chosen by the client or, sometimes — as when public organizations are involved — by a committee. The program phase is the time for determining how that choice will be made and how the architect will interact with the client or committee during the selection as well as during the design, execution, and installation of the craftsmen's work. It is important to determine in this phase whether the craftsmen are to be selected by the architect or interior designer with the client's approval, or by some other method, and, if so, how. These are important issues to be resolved by the conclusion of the program phase.

The most successfully integrated crafts projects have been those in which the architect or interior designer was either entirely responsible for, or intimately involved in, the selection, design, and installation processes. The embellishment or detail provided by the craftsmen must, of course, relate to the space in which it is incorporated. The success of an architectural environment, after all, depends on the comfortable interrelationship of all its elements.

If the client has a particular craftsman whose work he wants, it is very helpful for the client to introduce the craftsman to the architect or interior designer at the outset. An arrangement then can be set up whereby the craftsman essentially works for the architect or interior designer who, in turn, reports to the client, even though the craftsman's contract may, in fact, be directly with the client.

Lintel designed by M. Robert Van Arsdale. This is an example of a craftsman willingly executing a motif that was not his own because the client, who lived in New Mexico, had a strong preference for a particular style.

In many public building projects, especially when outside funding for craft or artwork is involved (as with percent-for-art programs), the art or craftwork is selected by a jury or committee. Unless it is thought out very carefully, this process can lead to a selection of objects that do not relate to the building or to the needs of the building users.

A serious problem arises from this method of selection when prestigious jurors are picked who live hundreds of miles from the building site. Many times these art experts are chosen because their names have status in the art world. Often they cannot read architectural plans and may not have an interest in or understanding of architectural spaces. Because they are brought in from the outside, they have no affinity for the particular locale or its inhabitants. Their assigned role is normally to guarantee only the quality of the artwork, and their standard is what they see as the cutting edge of innovation in the international art scene at that particular point in time. What is more, they may have a patronizing attitude toward the people — especially the locals — who will be the ultimate users of the building and who will view the art placed there for their enlightenment.

To make matters worse, the architect, or often a committee, sometimes chooses sites for the work before the craftsmen are selected but after the working drawings have been completed. An architect who doesn't know in advance that art or architectural crafts are to be used in his building is forced to use a postage-stamp approach to finding locations for these embellishments.

When dollar values are assigned these arbitrarily selected sites, artists and craftsmen working in many different media (with great variations in production costs) end up competing for commissions they either cannot afford to carry out or for which they are very much overpaid. This happens because uninformed jurors or committees — and no one can be an expert on all aspects of crafts or art — do not know the cost of the processes or materials used by different craftsmen. Slides or photographs submitted by craftsmen and artists for jurying (and by which their work is selected) often show work that costs more to produce than the current project will pay. The competing craftsmen may have less expensive solutions in mind than those shown in their examples, and these solutions may not be the appropriate ones for the site. If they aren't, many problems arise. (It goes without saying that artists and craftsmen should never be asked to bid on jobs in the traditional way. Automatically awarding the contract to the lowest bidder will not necessarily produce the right solution for the situation.)

After such a committee makes its choices, the architect and client are left to deal with the selected artists and craftsmen. They must try to make something rational out of what was selected: something that fits the budget, works with the building, and is acceptable to the eventual users of the space.

Often the public ends up with art that it doesn't understand and reacts by saying percent-for-art programs are only subsidies for undeserving artists — a poor use of tax money. The building often doesn't hold together visually, and the artists and craftsmen are restricted by the already defined spaces and budgets. The extremity of the disaster is relative only to the size of the egos involved — the egos of the administrators, the jurors, the architects, and finally the artists and craftsmen themselves. When little effort is made to work as a team, each party fights to have his own statement be the one that stands out, and the whole project can end up less than successful.

If a jury or selection committee is essential and if the opportunity for art or craft commissions must be made open to all artists and designer-craftsmen in a particular area, the following is a general format that can be adapted to various situations to increase the chances for success.

1. If at all possible, send a prospectus describing the project to eligible artists and/or designer-craftsmen during the program or concepts phase. Talk about the ultimate use of the building, the quality of construction, and the overall scope and image of the project. No plans, of course, should be sent, since none would exist. (Even if the project is past the concepts phase, plans should not be sent.)

2. Request five or ten slides of each craftsman's work. Three examples of previously completed installations — one shot of each in context, and a detail from each — plus a few other slides of the craftsman's choice will give a good idea of his or her capabilities.

To give the architect, interior designer, and contractor some idea of how each craftsman conducts business, ask him to make statements about the following or similar subjects: price range, availability of quantity pricing, minimum order requirements (if any), deposit, return, cancellation and warranty policies, shipping and installation policies, range of flexibility in finishes, weight, thickness, and color, and maintenance and repair procedures.

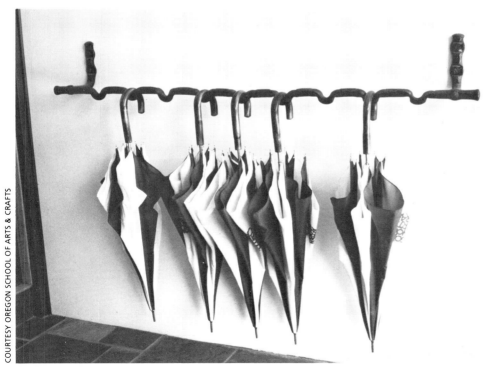

This umbrella rack was blacksmith Phillip Baldwin's solution to a school director's dilemma—a surplus of scattered umbrellas—due to the frequent rainfall in the Northwest.

11

3. Include on the jury the architects, interior designer, and client. Some successful art-in-public-places juries have been made up of the architect and members of the lay public, including the proposed building occupants. A separate prescreening by art experts will have taken place beforehand to assure the artistic merit of the work to be chosen. This method has worked well in situations where a state arts commission has administered the arts funds and felt obliged to guarantee the quality of work being supported by public funds. In one instance, a local lay jury initially wanted the work of a local craftsman used but changed its mind when it saw his work alongside other work accepted by the pre-screening jury.

Furthermore, involving local people in the selection process helps create an esprit de corps and a pride of ownership. Recently, in Colorado and in Oregon, members of juries for artwork became so interested in the projects they were judging that they volunteered to raise additional funds so there could be handmade instead of factory-made building components.

In Colorado, the architect was commissioned to design a no-frills, very economical laboratory building for the Orchard Growing Industry at Colorado State University. He wanted some adornment and was delighted when percent-for-art funds made art in his building mandatory. He was even more delighted when the selection committee, made up of local people, became so excited about the project that it volunteered to raise money to have a craftsman make hand-carved doors out of the fruit trees that were cut down to make room for the building.

In Oregon, a day lodge is being built next to historic Timberline Lodge to handle the increased day use of the area. The jury was to select five major pieces of art for the new structure. A local person on the jury volunteered to mobilize the community and raise funds to entirely furnish the new Wy 'East Day Lodge with the work of Northwest craftsmen.

4. Before the actual jurying begins, the jury should spend some time with the architect and client going over the basic programmed use of the building and the concept for its organization and image. If at all possible, the jurying should take place during the program or concepts phases.

5. Show all the slides of each craftsman at the same time, so that the jury can have an immediate understanding of the overall quality and style of his work. Ten projectors can be rented, if necessary, and the jurors can help advance the slides.

Strong personalities on the jury can have excessive influence. One way around the overly outspoken juror is to have at least the first couple of rounds silently juried. That way, by the time discussion begins, the more timid personalities are familiar with the work and can defend their support of it more easily. Simple tally sheets can be drawn up and scores 1 – out, 2 – mediocre, 4 – good, and 5 – terrific can be established so that at the end of each round of evaluation a certain number of entries are eliminated without much fuss. (A score of 3 is not used because it is neither positive nor negative.)

In the first rounds there is usually a high degree of consensus, even when a lay jury is reviewing work with an architect or interior designer. Good work can almost always be distinguished from mediocre. In a case involving a dairy commission building in Colorado, the building occupants on the jury were sure — if they *had* to have art — that what they wanted on the front of their building was a traditional mural depicting lifelike cows. During the selection process they completely changed their minds and chose a high-tech steel sculpture to go with their brand new high-tech building. They then went to their colleagues, defending the abstract piece.

Before *any* evaluating is done, however, it is a good idea to run through all the submissions; then everyone knows the total scope of the work from which the selections have to be made.

6. Ask the jurors to make their selections of designer-craftsmen to be involved in the project based on the quality of the work submitted (unless a prescreening is held for this purpose) and the appropriateness of the work to the building and its proposed use. The craftsman's design ability and the materials he uses are what are important. He may ultimately be asked to use his materials in an entirely new way, or he may be asked to use his design ability in an entirely new medium. (Successful examples of this approach were eye-catching banners designed by a stained-glass artist for a

Frank Boyden, a potter who had been making raku inserts for handmade stoves, designed this steel and ceramic wall panel for a hotel.

public mall, and brushed stainless-steel panels used to cover an entire building surface by a sculptor who previously had worked exclusively in stoves and sculptures.)

7. Tell the selected craftsmen that they have been chosen for *possible* participation. While contractors are used to bidding on jobs, craftsmen and artists are used to being approached only when clients are sure a project is certain and a particular artist's or craftsman's work is wanted. Bidding is not part of the designer-craftsman's world.

8. If an outside funding source is involved, send slides or photographs by the selected craftsmen to that funding source. Explain that as many of the selected craftsmen as possible will be used, depending on the amount of funds available and the size, location, and medium of the solution mutually agreed upon (by the architect or interior designer, craftsman, and client).

Once the funding is secure, the architect or interior designer and craftsman are brought together, and sites, materials, architect's or interior designer's concepts, and budgets are discussed.

The ideal situation, of course, is for the architect or interior designer to work with a consultant for architectural crafts who understands the needs of architects, interior designers, and craftsmen throughout the whole project. If a crafts consultant can be involved, many questions about structural needs and the quality and nature of materials used by craftsmen can be answered before commissioning particular craftsmen. A good consultant recommends appropriate craftsmen but does not push people in his own stable. He has access to craftsmen throughout his region and knows what is going on across the country. He can put together slide presentations of craftsmen working in various materials or organize competitions to select craftsmen so that architects and interior designers can see the variety of possibilities available for solving particular problems. A crafts consultant understands the limitations and possibilities within the craft field, and quite often he can come up with unorthodox suggestions — including new or unexpected combinations of materials that might not occur to either the architect or the craftsmen. He understands the processes and problems of most media and of having work installed, and he knows what craftwork generally costs. In many cases, he knows the particular working habits of individual craftsmen and their reputations for producing on time. Because many consultants work on an hourly basis for the architect or the client and do not receive a commission on the work eventually purchased, they can usually supply work to the client at lower than gallery prices.

There are only a handful of them in the country, but good consultants for architectural crafts have the skills to orchestrate the jury process and facilitate meetings and agreement among architect or interior designer, client, and craftsmen, to draw up contracts, and to oversee installation. When such a consultant is involved in a project at the program phase, he can give invaluable advice on how to plan for craftsmen's work early in the process, when the building itself is being planned. Because he is familiar with the materials and processes used by craftsmen, he can explain them to the architect. He can also explain the architect's point of view to the craftsmen. The best consultant excludes no one from the field of crafts when looking for the right craftsman for a project. He is just as comfortable working with university-trained designer-craftsmen as he is with metal fabricators or bricklayers.

If crafts consultants are not available to locate craftsmen, other avenues can be used. Galleries, craft schools, arts commissions, and university art departments can be of some help in finding craftsmen who affiliate with organizations. The Yellow Pages and various business directories will help locate others. Sometimes unions have lists they will give out, and many architects and designers have lists of their own.

Certainly, if the architect or interior designer knows what craftsmen he wants to use, he should bring them into the project as soon as possible. The client can then approve his selection, and all three can begin working together to develop the concept or "big idea" of the building.

It is in the concepts phase — when major ideas are offered and tested, and when discussion about the relationship of the building to the landscape and about the nature of the interior takes place — that the craftsmen should be included. By the end of this phase there is a rough idea of the building's size, scale, and shape; the basic organization of the spaces

Calligrapher Tim Girvin designed all the signs for the Oregon School of Arts and Crafts, putting his letters on enameled steel panels. Marge Hammond, who works in concrete, designed and executed the school's cigarette and trash containers.

within it are known.

Hopefully, by the end of the concepts phase the craftsmen will have been selected. At least the architect and client should have some idea of the

Architect Walter Gordon and landscape architect Wallace K. Huntington worked with woodworker Jay Wilson to create this entry on a busy street in Portland.

craftsmen available and appropriate for the project so that they can begin planning with them in mind.

It should be clear at this point for whom the craftsmen will be working, with whom their contracts will be made, and to whom they will look for payment. If possible, contracts should be written authorizing the craftsmen to begin design work on the project, and an advance should be made to each craftsman to cover his design fee. This is usually between 10 and 30 percent of the total fee, which should be established now unless it is for a small project of $500 or less. In that case, the initial payment is usually 50 percent.

When the craftsmen report directly to the crafts consultant and/or architect or interior designer, projects seem to work most smoothly. The architect and interior designer and landscape architect can then present the overall design solution to the client, along with their ideas about energy conservation or building materials, and deal with any subsequent change orders in an orderly manner. Although the contract is usually drawn up between the craftsmen and the client (since it is the client who is paying for the craftwork) it is really best for the project if the craftsmen report to the interior designer or architect in matters of design. The architect, interior designer, or crafts consultant usually approves all invoices submitted by the craftsmen for payment by the client. Some interior designers, especially on smaller jobs, frequently hire and pay craftsmen directly, adding on a commission before billing the client.

Because each job is so individual, some designer-craftsmen — particularly on bigger jobs — have difficulty estimating the overall cost of a job before they have spent a lot of time on the design. (Others know more or less how much they need to charge per square or linear foot.) This is a difficult situation and one which will require a certain amount of patience until the designer-craftsmen as a group become more adept at estimating costs. This is one area in which a crafts consultant can be especially useful.

While variety and surprise are sought-after elements in interior design and architecture, successful projects tend to be those where all the professionals have communicated from the beginning and worked as a team. Interiors, exteriors, and actual structural elements of a building are all related. A hand-carved entry door, for example, has an impact on the landscape, the interior, and the building itself. However, without successful lighting, the effect of the door can be lost at night.

The issue of how much influence the architect or interior designer should have on the design of the craftwork for a building inevitably comes up. It is a given fact that architects, interior designers, and designer-craftsmen all have strong egos. The opportunity to make a permanent visual impact is, after all, what draws many to the field of design. Some clients have strong ideas themselves and want to have a hand in designing the craftwork, too. It is true that too many cooks can spoil the soup, but sometimes the skillful inclusion of many ingredients can produce a gourmet's delight. It is extremely important for craftsmen, clients, architects, and interior designers to be willing to listen to each other and to be openly committed to producing the best results, even if it means including other people's ideas. The best results — the ones that satisfy over time — are the ones produced by people who care about the overall end product and how it relates to its environment.

By the end of the schematic design phase, the preliminary design of the craftwork should be known. Since by then elevations, cross sections, floor plans, room configurations, and view lines from windows have been defined; building materials and colors have been decided upon; and there is a basic notion of how furniture will be arranged, it is easier to see how the craftsmen's work — whether in the form of particular building materials or as decorative or useful objects — will fit into the total scheme of things.

It is also at this point that any coordination with mechanical, electrical, lighting, plumbing, or other detailing can be arranged, and adaptations to the needs of the craftsmen and vice versa can be worked out.

Ideally, the craftsmen should submit their final design proposals during the design development phase so that they can be discussed and coordinated along with the rest of the project design put forth by the architect, landscape architect, interior designer, and mechanical, electrical, lighting, and other consultants. All aspects of the construction of the building should be defined at this point, and specific carpeting, furnishings, and plant material should be chosen. Then the craftsmen can produce a piece of work that is truly integrated into its environment.

At the end of the design development phase, the craftsmen's designs either should be accepted and the craftsmen given authorization to begin work, or the designs should be rejected and the craftsmen asked to submit other solutions or

An example of a successful collaboration between a blacksmith and an interior designer is this steel and brass knocker by Phillip Baldwin and Mirza Dickel for a house in McMinnville, Oregon.

to conclude their relationships with the project. If the craftsmen are authorized to proceed, they should be paid another 33 to 45 percent of the total fee negotiated in the original contract. Minor revisions that alter small details of the approved designs are covered by the design fee. Additional contracts must be negotiated if substantial revisions are made that alter the concept or spirit of the designs.

If the design quality and workmanship of the craftsmen's previous work was approved by the client and architect during the concepts phase of the project and if the craftsmen were actively involved in the development of the conceptual and schematic phases of design, the final designs they submit will usually be acceptable. Before the final designs are submitted, the craftsmen should have had ample opportunity to talk over informal proposals with the architect or interior designer and to have elicited opinions about the direction of their ideas. Unfortunately, conflicts do occasionally arise that cannot be resolved. That is why it is most advisable to make a final decision about the craftsmen at the conclusion of the design development phase.

If a relationship with a craftsman has to be terminated, this is the right time to do it. He has been paid for his design time and has had the opportunity to make a well-thought-out proposal. The amount of money paid for the unused design is negligible in terms of the total budget, and there are a minimum of hurt feelings. While the design fee may seem high, the difference between a well-

thought-out design and a bad one is, in most cases, the critical difference between a successful and a disastrous project. Workmanship is important, but no matter how good the workmanship, a piece will fail if it is poorly designed.

When a craftsman is replaced, it is important that everyone involved cooperate to fully inform the new person about the rest of the project. Even when a situation is ideal, there will have to be a lot of cooperation to keep everyone informed and up to schedule. Flexibility and the ability to cope with difficulties are essential ingredients to the success of building projects. Designer-craftsmen work differently from other craftsmen. For example, craftsmen in the trades sometimes work for a larger

Joyce Newman installing Town Meeting, *a ceramic stoneware frieze in Littleton, Colorado.*

company whose principals are doing the negotiating. Sometimes it eventually becomes advisable for the architect or interior designer to deal directly with those craftsmen who will actually be doing the work.

When the construction documents phase has arrived and all the major design issues have been solved, and the details are finally put on paper in the form of working drawings, craftsmen can see if their work is being incorporated where and how they thought it would be. The drawings and written specifications should include all the information pertaining to the inclusion of craftwork so that when they are put out to bid or given to a contractor, the inclusion of the craftwork can be calculated accurately into the construction costs. Without this information at the bidding stage, there will inevitably be subsequent change orders that can be costly and frustrating to the client, craftsmen, architect, and contractor. Coordination among the craftsmen, architect or interior designer, and draftsman is therefore especially critical throughout the design development and construction documents phases.

During the construction phase, if they are involved in installation, the craftsmen become, to a certain degree, subcontractors. So as soon as the overall construction bid has been concluded and a particular contractor is involved, it is important to introduce the craftsmen to the contractor and also to work out details pertaining to the date of installation and coordination with other subcontractors whose work relates to that of the craftsmen. Immediately upon installation the craftsmen should be paid the balance of their fees.

While the contractor may be responsible for the coordination and timing of the installation of the craftwork, the craftsmen's contracts should stay with the client, and they should still, for the most part, be reporting to the architect or interior designer. It is only when an architect is not involved that a craftsman would report to the contractor or the client.

RICK PAULSON

Keith Jellum (left) welded this steel gate in his studio and, with the help of Colin Page, installed it at the Oregon School of Arts and Crafts, where over twenty craftsmen were involved in producing elements of architectural detail. Works of two other craftsmen are shown here: a sign by calligrapher Tim Girvin and a cast concrete refuse container by Marge Hammond.

COURTESY OREGON SCHOOL OF ARTS & CRAFTS

Keith Jellum's gate after installation.

What Craftsmen Need to Know

This section is directed specifically to designer-craftsmen. However, it may be useful to architects and interior designers in their dealings with craftsmen.

As Designers:

Craftsmen work in a way that is not often duplicated in any other part of our culture, sometimes using materials unusual in and of themselves. Craftsmen add mind and spirit to the work of the hand to create unique solutions. Some craftsmen are trained specifically in technique; others have had strong backgrounds in design. To work successfully in an architectural project, a craftsman must bring all his knowledge and ability to it. When the craftsman and architect or interior designer listen to each other's ideas about design, materials, and color, they not only develop a good working relationship, they also allow for the possibility of growth.

In architectural commissions, an ability and willingness to listen to the needs and desires of the client and to perceive the vision of the architect or interior designer are essential. A designer-craftsman is constantly growing and changing and has a real need to express his current ideas in his work, but an architectural commission is simply not the place for this unless the end result is really going to complement its environment.

Many architects and designers are not familiar with the restrictions of particular crafts media, and they don't necessarily know what type of work is best suited for specific locations. Some glass artists prefer north windows; many textiles will deteriorate in direct sunlight; and exposed ironwork needs certain maintenance. It is best if the craftsman can communicate such things to the interior designer or architect early in the project, especially if a consultant for architectural crafts is not involved.

The ability to draw is probably one of the most useful tools a craftsman can have. The craftsman who draws not only sees better but understands more clearly how shapes and lines relate to each other. Too often, craftsmen are so seduced by their media that they never take time to learn to draw. But potters who take life drawing make better pots — it is a fact. Jewelers often learn a particular kind of rendering that shows off the sparkle of a diamond, but few of them can draw, and it shows in their work. Although technique is important in executing a leaded-glass window, the window's success depends on its design and the selection of materials that make up the design. Being able to conceive and draw that design is critical.

Drawing, especially life drawing, also forces the craftsman to see bigger relationships and inter-relationships in his work. Woodworkers are fascinated by joinery and the tools used to accomplish it. While their craftsmanship is often superb, some are so absorbed in working on detail that the overall designs of pieces are unsuccessful. Drawing will help teach a craftsman the value of seeing detail as part of a whole. It also helps any craftsman see the relationship of his proposed piece to the architectural setting for which it is being designed.

Drawing for the purpose of explaining concepts to oneself and others is one of the best means of communication there is in the design field. An interior designer or architect and craftsman sitting down at a table and conversing through the medium of lead on paper can produce amazing solutions.

In the first stages of working with an architect or interior designer, roughly drawn ideas help both parties reach an understanding. Once there is a general understanding and the craftsman has had a chance to work up an idea, he should prepare a proposal in as professional a manner as possible. The proposal will vary from medium to medium and craftsman to craftsman; however, clarity is of the essence.

If the craftsman already has been commissioned, a drawing to scale of the proposed piece in color, a rendering of it in context, and some samples of the materials to be used generally will make an adequate proposal. Sometimes a scale model or a life-size part of a proposed piece — constructed of the materials that are being proposed for the project — is appropriate. These are choices the craftsman needs to make and they depend on the nature of the client and the project. A person remodeling his bathroom needs a different sort of presentation than does the president of the board of a huge hotel chain.

If a craftsman is not selected by the procedures outlined in this book, he can be faced with the task of both selling himself and making a proposal in one fell swoop. This, unfortunately, is often the case. Salesmanship is needed, and proposal submission and marketing become intertwined.

The best proposal in this situation is composed of detailed models in full color — using as many of the actual materials as possible — and a set of color slides or photographs of previously executed commissions of similar scope and size. This should be accompanied by well-organized, concise promotional material on the craftsman himself.

Marketing is a process that should never be neglected. Some craftsmen make detailed scale models of their proposed installations, including cardboard people standing about in the space. These are photographed in color, and then the slides are projected on large screens to clients. These presentations are quite impressive and allow clients and architects to understand exactly what is being proposed by craftsmen. One craftsman, unable to

John Rogers prepared this model, complete with cardboard people, to show his client what he proposed for the side of a building in Tacoma.

make a personal appearance, sent a synchronized tape and slide presentation that outlined the thought process he had gone through to arrive at the proposal he was making. It cost him close to $2,000 in slides and model making. Some of the slides showed samples of parts of his proposed piece in which he actually used the materials he was proposing. He got the commission.

Somewhere along the line, the craftsman is usually faced with the need to interpret architectural drawings. If he is not brought into a project until the schematics or the working drawings are completed, he will have to gain a sense of the project largely from these drawings. Even if the craftsman has been involved from the outset, he will need to be able to determine if his work is being accurately incorporated into the scheme of things when his proposals are included in the working drawings. Cases are known in which walls have been moved in the time between the acceptance of a craftsman's proposal and the approval of the working drawings.

In the fast-track process, where construction on part of a project is begun before the building is completely designed, the craftsman has to be especially adaptive. This process is used in periods of high inflation or in areas with extreme weather conditions where construction is possible only a few months of the year. Usually a single contractor is involved in a negotiated bid situation. He agrees to begin pouring the foundation while plans for the total project are still in process. He will have detailed working drawings of the foundation and only schematics, or less, of the rest. Sometimes there is a different contractor for each part of the project, which makes it even more complicated. Craftsmen involved in these projects do well to understand the ideal overall design and construction process, but they must realize that it is modified for fast-track projects. It is necessary to work within the constraints of the situation, and no two situations are alike.

As Businessmen:

Craftsmen may produce earthshaking work, but if no one knows about it, it will stay in the minds and studios of the creators. A craftsman is really a small businessman, and most small businessmen have to

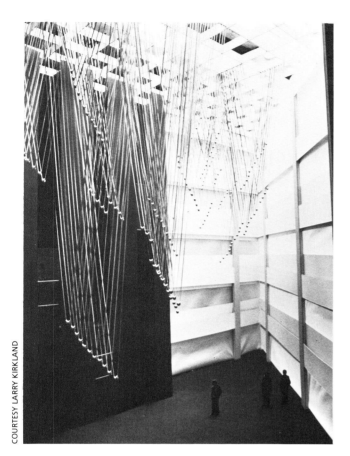

Photograph of a model made by Larry Kirkland. The photograph — originally a slide — was part of a proposal to the Shell Oil Company for a piece that was subsequently executed in a new research facility in Houston. Kirkland and John Rogers were charged with designing something for the sixty-foot-high atrium that would relate to Shell's research activities.

Echoes, *designed and installed by John Rogers and Larry Kirkland for Shell Oil Company, interprets sound-wave patterns used in the search for oil and natural gas. The piece consists of over two hundred two-inch-wide straps held together at the bottom by cast porcelain pendants.*

promote themselves or their businesses. What a craftsman — especially a designer-craftsman — has to sell is uniqueness, style, quality, and the ability to do one-of-a-kind projects that industry cannot afford to do.

Today's public is attracted to the work of craftsmen because it is unique. At the same time, people are accustomed to slickness, and they expect professionalism. The glass craftsman who presents a neatly typed contract and who calls two days in advance to remind the client that he will be installing his window at the agreed-upon time is talked about glowingly at many a cocktail party thereafter.

Although an address scribbled on plain paper or on a paper bag are ways of communicating one's identity, personalized stationery and business cards

help create an image of stability and visual awareness. An "identity package" can be designed by the craftsman himself or by a graphic designer. In many instances, the visual impression made by the stationery and business card will represent the craftsman. A poorly designed package is sometimes worse than none at all.

The cost of an identity package will usually involve design work, typesetting, printing, paper, and envelopes. The simplest all-purpose combination is 8½-by-11 letterhead with plain second sheets, standard business envelopes, and business cards. The letterhead can be used for letters, proposal presentations, contracts, invoices, resumés, and price lists. The blank second sheets are for two- and three-page letters and lists. They

Bridget Beattie McCarthy 7277 Southwest Barnes Road   Portland, Oregon 97225   503-292-4549

Bridget Beattie McCarthy

Bridget Beattie McCarthy

Consultant for Architectural Crafts
7277 Southwest Barnes Road   Portland, Oregon 97225
503-292-4549

Earth & Fire

pottery by Nancy Jacquot

1072 Empinado Drive   Laramie, Wyoming 82070   (307) 742-2785

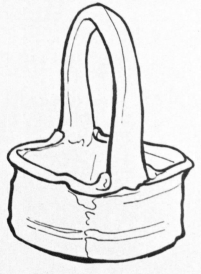

Earth & Fire
pottery by Nancy Jacquot

Earth & Fire

pottery by Nancy Jacquot

Laramie, Wyoming

(307) 742-2785

23

are necessary if the stationery is not white. Business cards need not be printed all alike. For a very small extra charge, half can be printed with slightly different copy so that a craftsman can sell himself as a production potter with one set of cards and as an architectural tile designer with the other.

It is not advisable to list everything the craftsman does on the business card. A brochure serves that purpose better. Or copy can always be typed on a white sheet of paper and then Xeroxed onto letterhead. This can look impressive, especially if the letterhead is a color, and it is an inexpensive substitute for a brochure. Color Xeroxing has a lot of possibilities, and many quick-print places can reduce copy inexpensively.

In a pinch, a rubber stamp with name, address, and phone number can be used to stamp up a pad of white note paper. The pad is easy to carry, and sheets can be torn off as needed. Notes can be written on these, and letters and invoices can be written on larger sheets that are stamped at the top.

To show their work, textile people and potters use slides almost exclusively; most woodworkers have envelopes filled with color snapshots; graphic designers carry about huge portfolios of completed jobs; and jewelers display examples of their work in black velvet boxes.

A good way to quickly and professionally show work to a client, architect, or interior designer is to have a loose-leaf or other binder filled with 8-by-10 black-and-white and color photographs of installations, plus a sheaf of slides that can be held up to the light, put on a light table, or actually projected. While many craftsmen are accustomed to working with slides — and they may be useful in some presentations — people are not always willing to view them to their best advantage. Therefore, the large color and black-and-white photographs, which a client can look at as he is talking to the craftsman, are often more effective. A resumé and any other promotional material about the craftsman completes the package. A simple brochure or price list left with the client after the presentation is a good way to be remembered.

Resumés should be concise and should accentuate the craftsman's professional background. High school awards for high jumping may be envied at the twentieth class reunion, but prospec-tive clients are more interested in the fact that the craftsman apprenticed to a famous European tapestry designer or made thirty-eight handmade sinks for a hotel in Alaska.

The craftsman's work itself is, of course, his best marketing tool. The world is crying out for quality and uniqueness. Craftsmen can market themselves, or they can work with consultants, marketing agents, architects, interior designers, galleries, or all of the above. A good gallery or a consultant specializing in architectural crafts has many contacts and can be invaluable in locating and dealing with clients, in landing commissions, and in making sales — saving the craftsman days of time.

It is sometimes difficult for beginning crafts-men to understand that galleries and consultants need to make money, too, and they often make the mistake of undercutting the very people who are marketing their work for them. Some people like to make craftwork and some people like to sell it. A good relationship can benefit both.

Until recently, most craftsmen established the price they needed to be paid for work and then added to this price a commission — to be paid to whomever was handling its promotion. If a crafts-man was famous and successful enough to have his own in-house promoters, he had them on his payroll. If a gallery or agent was directly involved in securing a particular commission or sale, then a certain percentage was given the gallery, even if the craftsman had not asked it to solicit work for him.

It has been the policy of many galleries to expect a smaller percentage if the craftsman arranges deals on his own and if he has a permanent relationship with a gallery. But they do expect a percentage. A commission, the galleries feel, should be paid the gallery or agent because it is the exposure that the craftsman is given by the gallery or agent that creates the demand for his work. In some cases this is true. Galleries work hard to push craftsmen in their stables.

There have always been art consultants, but in the seventies — along with consultants in all fields — their number increased dramatically. Today, most of them handle free-standing art or craftwork and operate in much the same way as galleries; some are even affiliated with galleries. There are, however, a very few art and craft consultants specializing in commission work. They usually receive an hourly fee from the architect or client to orchestrate the inclusion of art or craftwork in a project. They promote the work of craftsmen and sell the whole concept of architectural crafts. They visit banks and telephone companies and hotels that are planning new buildings and work at convincing the people in charge that crafts will enhance their buildings.

Selling work directly to consumers from the studio at reduced prices discourages them from buying through galleries and consultants, and eats up the craftsman's valuable design and production time. It is better if he has wholesale and discount prices only for galleries, agents, consultants, and contractors. Then these people, who use the commission arrangement, can add their markup to the price (from 15 to 50 percent, depending on whether they are interior designers, contractors, or galleries). The craftsman should charge retail consumers the full marked-up price to compensate himself for the time used to make the sale, and he should encourage them to patronize the galleries, agents, consultants, and contractors working in his behalf.

Once a gallery, consultant, interior designer, or contractor has contacted a client regarding the work of a craftsman, that craftsman should never try to deal directly with the client. This is a mistake craftsmen often make in their desire to eliminate the middleman. It is, however, the kiss of death in terms of any further relationships with that middleman. A cabinetmaker being considered by a contractor or interior designer for a job should never submit an estimate directly to the client. The cabinetmaker's estimate goes to the contractor or interior designer who is bidding the entire job and is handling all the negotiations with the client. The craftsman is a subcontractor reporting to the contractor or interior designer.

Some craftsmen sell without a gallery or an agent and do quite well; however, they are usually craftsmen who have spent a lot of time promoting themselves and who have reached a point where they are supported by one or two large commissions a year. The craftsman who each year does two stained-glass windows at $50,000 each may not need someone else to promote his work as much as the craftsman who is trying to make a year's living doing tile and sink installations.

A contract is not only a legal safeguard; it is also a communication tool and, to some extent, a marketing tool. When a contract is being negotiated and drawn up, the opportunity for communication between the craftsman and client is greatest. The simpler the contract is, the less awesome it is to the client. Avoid discouraging him with too many conditions. Some have canceled projects because the artist wanted a percentage every time the house was sold or because he wanted some control over his work after it was installed.

The client might be a contractor or interior designer or someone other than the eventual owner of the work. Make sure that as a craftsman you always report to the person with whom your contract was originally drawn up. Do not make the mistake of communicating with the client about a problem if your contract is with the contractor. First, such communication is inappropriate and, second, change orders can wreak havoc in a project if they are done without the approval of the contractor or interior designer in charge.

Basically, what a contract should do is state clearly for the craftsman and client the nature of the work, how much it will cost, how and when the craftsman will be paid, and how design review and installation will be handled. It can be simple or detailed and should be tailored to each situation. Some cases call for more detailed protection of the craftsman; some clients require special clauses. The following is a prototype from which other contracts can be custom-made for a particular situation — and it is advisable to tailor each contract to each situation. This one should not be used as is, and either or both the craftsman's or client's lawyer should be consulted at the outset.

COMMISSION AGREEMENT (SAMPLE CONTRACT)

Craftsman
Name: _____
Address: _____

Owner
Name: _____
Address: _____

Organization
(optional)

The board of directors of the XYZ Organization has authorized J. Doe to enter into this contract on behalf of the Owner and to approve the Craftsman's designs, to authorize execution and installation, and to make payments.

(In situations where an organization is involved, be sure that the party or committee with whom the craftsman is dealing has the authority to make decisions for the body at large.)

Description of Work

This commission includes the design, execution, and installation of
_____ .

(State here whatever is necessary to determine the scope of the work: for example, size, materials, where it will be placed in the building.)

Design

The Craftsman will submit one model or drawing with samples of proposed materials. It is understood that the Owner has seen samples of the Craftsman's previous work, has discussed with him the general requirements, mood, content, and architecture of the building, and is willing to place faith in the Craftsman's ability to make an acceptable design.

(Be sure to stress one *model or drawing so that the owner does not demand many before accepting the design.)*

Minor revisions of the submitted design that have been mutually agreed upon, and would alter small details only, are covered by the design fee.

If the Owner requests substantial revisions that would alter the concept or spirit of the design, such revisions are subject to negotiation of an additional fee.

The Craftsman's design will be copyrighted to the Craftsman and will remain his property. The Craftsman retains sole right of execution of his designs.

Design Acceptance
(optional)

(If the architect or someone other than the owner should be involved, say so here.)

Design Completion
(optional)

Date: _____

Fee

Total fee for the work is to be $ _____ .

Payment Schedule

First payment of $ _____ is a design fee and is payable immediately on signing of this agreement by both parties and is nonrefundable regardless of whether the design is accepted.

Second payment of $ _____ is payable at the time of acceptance of the design by the Owner.

Final payment of $ _____ is payable on the day of completion of installation of the Work.

(Basically, the total fee is divided into three payments: for design, execution, and completion. If the job is over $15,000, however, four or more payments may be preferable, perhaps with the third made on invoice from the craftsman when 50 percent of the work is completed. The owner may want to have a representative inspect the work at that time. Simply tailor the contract to the particular situation. Some craftsmen work only on a one-third, one-third, one-third basis, while others ask 10 percent for the design fee and 45 percent each for execution and completion. From a craftsman's point of view, the bigger the design fee the better, because the client is more likely to go ahead with the execution, having invested quite a bit in the project already. A client may look at it differently. Good judgment will have to be used here, but in any case remember that the best execution cannot cover up a poor design.)

Method of Payment

All payments are to be made by certified check and sent by registered mail to the Craftsman at the following address _____ (optional) with the exception of the last payment, which will be hand-delivered on the day of completion of the installation.

(The certified check/registered mail requirement may turn off some clients. Craftsmen sometimes specify this for out-of-state situations where committees and other complications make this safeguard desirable.)

Crating and Shipping
(optional)

The Craftsman will arrange crating and bill the Owner for crating costs, along with other reimbursables. The Work will be sent freight collect, and the insurance in transit is the responsibility of the Owner.

(What needs to be established is who will do the crating and shipping, who will pay for it, and how will it be insured.)

Site Preparation
(optional)

(State clearly here what is expected of the owner in terms of preparing the site for installation of the work. Are special structural elements in the architecture called for? Must an area be cleaned or painted? Make sure site preparation is at the owner's cost.)

Installation

The Craftsman will (will not) be responsible for installation. The installation may take a number of days and the Owner will need to provide the following equipment (for example, scaffolding). Or installation will be done by members of the ABC Union and a separate contract will be drawn up between Z. Smith and the Owner. The Craftsman will oversee installation. Installation will take place on the following date(s)_____.

Reimbursables
(optional)

The Craftsman will be reimbursed for coach airfare, ground transportation, meals, hotel accommodations, etc. for the number of days necessary to carry out the business at hand.

(Make a list of reimbursables —for example, insurance and crating —to give the owner an idea of what will be charged. The owner may demand a ceiling figure.)

Anticipated schedule of visits to the site: _____

Delinquent Payment

If the Owner fails to make a payment when due, a finance charge of 1½ percent (18 percent per annum) will be assessed against the unpaid balance due and work may cease until the payments are brought up to date.

The completion dates for the phase of work in progress will be postponed by a period equal to that of the delinquency.

Warranty
(optional)

The Craftsman warrants the Work for one year against defects of workmanship and materials from the time of installation and will replace or repair any part of the work which is shown to be defective during that period.

The Owner has to notify the Craftsman within ten days of discovering the defect (optional).

Arbitration
(optional)

Disputes arising out of this agreement which cannot be otherwise settled are subject to binding arbitration under the rules of the American Arbitration Association (optional).

(The American Arbitration Association handles disputes in a quick manner, and its decisions normally are final. The use of this group can save weeks of dealing with the traditional court system and many dollars. Some parties in a dispute, nonetheless, prefer to use the courts.)

When applicable, the arbitration will rely on the laws of the home state of the Craftsman.

(This will save expensive research and possible travel by the craftsman's lawyer.)

Craftsman: _____
Date: _____

Representative of the Owner: _____
Date: _____

Some craftsmen include some of the following clauses pertaining to the resale, repair, and copying of their work as well.

The client agrees that if in the future the client does sell the work during the life of the craftsman, the client will pay the craftsman the sum of 15 percent of the appreciated value of the work.

The client will make all reasonably necessary repairs and restoration of the work. Where possible the craftsman will be consulted as to his or her recommendations with regard to all such repairs and restorations which are made during the life-time of the craftsman. To the extent practicable and in accordance with accepted principles of professional conservation, the craftsman will be given the opportunity to accomplish such repairs and restorations and will be paid a reasonable fee for any such services.

The craftsman reserves all rights to reproduce or to copy the work except in cases in which the client wishes to reproduce photographs of the work for noncommercial purposes and provided that any such reproductions be accompanied by a copyright notice to the craftsman.

Some states have statutes pertaining to the above subjects. A lawyer should be consulted about them locally.

In all his dealings, the craftsman should try to be as businesslike as possible. A typewriter should be used so documents will look professional. When sending slides or proposals, a simple cover letter should be included stating what it is that is being sent. It should never be assumed that because a contract has been signed a client is going to pay automatically. It is customary to send a bill, which can be typed on letterhead as follows:

Janet Sylvester
Woodworks
22 Elm Street, Hot Springs, Arizona

October 21, 1981

Blue Sky Hotel
31 Baywater Street
Palisades, Nevada

Attn: John Pensner, Executive Vice President

As per contract agreement of August 31, 1981, the second payment upon acceptance of the design of the lounge bar and stools, which took place on October 20, 1981.

Total due: $9,000—

Thank you

Mary McDuncan
The Pottery
Route 2, Pocatello, Idaho

January 7, 1982

Joan Davidson
Designed Interiors
6842 NW Placier Way
Appleton, Washington

Three hand-thrown blue-and-white stoneware sinks delivered to plumber at McBeth residence on January 3, 1982.

3 @ $225.00 each   total due: $675.00

Thank you

Henry Henderson
Architectural Glass Design
1 Main Street, Logan, Washington

June 15, 1982

Eighth Congregational Church
48 Summit Avenue
Hanson, Utah

Attn: Hewitt Ross, Chairman Building Committee

As per contract agreement of July 17, 1981, reimbursement for:

Construction of eight (8) crates for shipping glass	$ 800.00
One (1) R/T coach airfare Portland, OR to Hanson, UT	338.21
Two nights at Grand Hotel with meals (June 6 and 7)	138.00
Total Due	$1,276.21

Thank you

As Subcontractors:

When the design has been approved and all the work that can be completed off the site is done, the work is ready for installation and/or on-site construction. Now the craftsman becomes a kind of subcontractor, sometimes subject, if challenged, to the rules surrounding other subcontractors. The crafts consultant, architect, or interior designer should introduce the craftsman to the general contractor as early as possible, and a delivery or installment date should be set. The craftsman should also know with what subcontractors he will be working.

If it is a closed-shop union situation, it will take a certain amount of explaining to convince some union representatives that the craftsman's work cannot be done by others. Usually designer-craftsmen do their installations alone or with their own assistants after the plumbers and electricians and carpenters and painters have gone, so the problem doesn't come up. However, if the craftsman does install his own work when union people are on the job or if, for example, a plumber has to work with a potter, it is best simply to call the craftsman the supplier who oversees the installation of his product. There is often no problem anyway. In fact, when handled well, the experience has been a treat for subcontractors, who frequently are bored with many of their jobs and are either intrigued by the craftsmen or are happy to exercise their expertise in installing something special.

The best way to handle problems that might come up at this point is to include everyone involved in the project in the whole experience. Explain that a designer-craftsman produces one-of-a-kind items or materials and that unions are not part of the world of artists or designer-craftsmen. If everyone is excited and positive and brings whoever is investigating the situation into the world of handmade crafts, most people will probably react positively. Almost everyone has had some experience that can be related to crafts — a grandmother who crochets, a brother who carves wood in his basement — and can become very enthusiastic about what is being done.

If all else fails and union or other people must be hired separately to do the installation, an additional contract needs to be drawn up between the owner or the contractor and the subcontractor. It must specify that the designer-craftsman or consultant for architectural crafts will be on hand to supervise.

Often installation takes a number of days, and sometimes it must be done in the middle of the night. This can happen when the craftwork is installed after the building is open to the public, and it can put the cost of labor at time and a half. This expense should be planned for when calculating the installation cost.

Having others install the work may seem complicated but, in the long run, it may be the best thing to do, especially when workers' compensation and liability are required for everyone working on

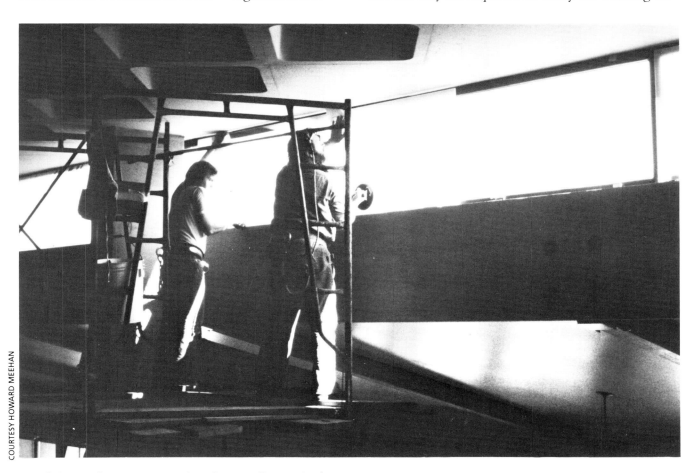

Noted glass craftsman Tim O'Neil (right) installing a piece by Howard Meehan in southern Oregon.

Bruce West assembling a brushed stainless-steel stove at the Oregon School of Arts and Crafts.

a site. For a craftsman to carry insurance on other independent contractors can be extremely unwieldy and expensive.

If the craftsman was originally employed by a contractor or interior designer as a subcontractor, he should continue to report to that person. If the eventual owner wants to make suggestions, any change orders, however miniscule, should be cleared with the contractor or interior designer. Change orders, no matter how unimportant they may appear, can throw a project off schedule and cost the contractor or interior designer many dollars. This is especially true in a bid situation, where the estimate has usually been carefully calculated to include enough time and materials to make a profit on the job and still make it financially attractive to the client.

The procedures that have been outlined in this book are by no means the only ways to get a job done.

They should be used as points of reference. Each situation is different and no two individuals are alike. The best working conditions are created by good communication, flexibility, efficient and sensible business practices, and a sense of trust and good will on the part of all concerned.

Because each situation is unique, each contract should be tailor-made. But, in every case, the craftsman should be involved early in a project. If that is not possible, everyone will need an unusual ability to cope with time limitations, physical difficulties, and personalities.

The author was recently involved in a project for which the integration of crafts was not even considered until the building was nearly completed. The department heads working for the occupant had not thought out their needs for fixtures and furniture. Communication among architect, occupant, and owners was sporadic. Yet, when the concept of substituting handmade objects for their commercial counterparts was suggested, everyone rallied around it, and — despite severe time pressures and a lack of prior planning — began working together to achieve a common goal.

Being open and friendly and having the aesthetic cohesiveness of an environment as everyone's goal are the keys to success. Owner, occupant, craftsman, architect, interior designer, landscape architect, and contractors can all help each other and can usually come up with solutions that please everybody.

Successfully Integrated Crafts

Architectural crafts lend themselves to all sorts of building situations. New buildings and renovations are both enhanced when crafts and the craftsmen's unique materials are incorporated in them. Institutional, commercial, and residential buildings all offer opportunities for the inclusion of either functional or ornamental work.

In all cases, of course, it is preferable to involve the craftsman as early in the design process as possible in order that all parties involved can work out mutually acceptable solutions for the placement and design of the work.

The result of a collaboration started early enough in the remodeling of the Executive Office Building in Salem, Oregon, so that Ed Carpenter could convince the architect to change his initial concept of a skylight to a clerestory window.

*Walter White designed this fire-engine
weather vane for Engine House #11
in Tacoma.*

*One of the rugs Barbara Hand of Montana has designed in consultation with
interior designers and clients.*

Mural-and-tile spillway by Barbara Grygutis for a pool and spa in a private residence in Tucson. As a statement about the visual illusion of the South-western landscape, the spillway demonstrates the similarities between two opposing elements — the desert and large bodies of water.

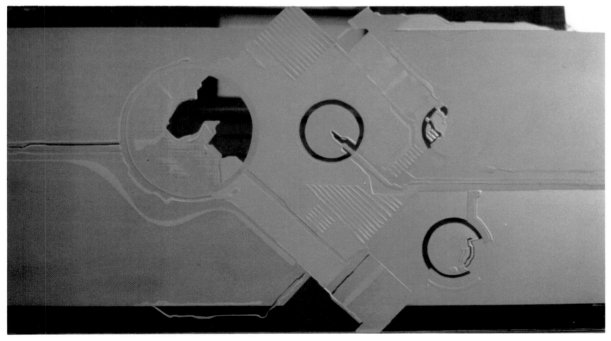

Howard Meehan of Portland sandblasts glass to form wall panels. This is a 4-by-6-foot detail.

Juan and Patricia Navarette of Taos,
New Mexico, designed and constructed
this adobe fireplace. Their work takes
into consideration both the structural
necessities and the aesthetic possibilities
that sculptured design can add to a room.

Fred Heidel's laminated
glass adds an illuminated
quality to the 300 square
feet it occupies in the Central
Mall Building in Salem,
Oregon. The six panels of
resin-laminated stained
glass are on both sides of
half-inch tempered plate.

A hanging globe of "illuminated clay" provides a unique lighting effect. Allan Kluber of Eugene, Oregon, works with colored porcelain clay bodies.

Harold Balazs of Spokane has worked with architects for years in many different media. This concrete fireplace was done for Kahneeta Lodge on the Warm Springs Indian Reservation in Oregon.

The shape of the individual tiles and the overall shape of the group were determined by the function of this fireplace apron by Georgia Sartoris of Denver.

Sandra Robishaw constructed Fiberglas molds for the concrete contractor to use in pouring this wall at the University of Southern Colorado in Pueblo, Colorado.

"Aguave" gate in Tucson designed by Keith Jellum to be used by both pedestrians and automobiles.

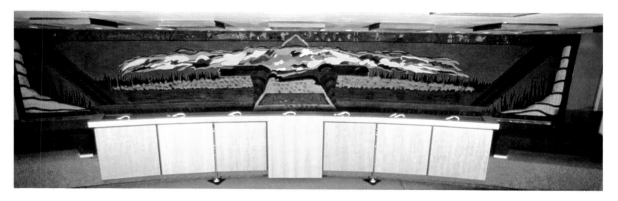

Through the Cottonwoods, One Could Hear the Games Being Played: *10-by-60-foot tapestry by Dana Boussard for the city hall in Boise. Boussard did extensive research into the history of the area and consulted with the architect on how to best use the space before she began work on this piece.*

Ken Williams designed this sculptured brick wall for the administration building of School District #60 in Pueblo.

Mahogany door in Albuquerque by Federico Armijo.

Craftsmen Whose Work Has Been Used in Architecture

When Western States Arts Foundation began to consider compiling this catalog, it was faced with the problem of photographing hundreds of objects, many installed, in hundreds of locations.

Since the cost of sending a consultant and a photographer on an extensive, nearly year-long expedition would be too expensive, the Foundation asked the craftsmen to send slides, photographs, and information about themselves to a jury. The resulting material was juried by architect Cab Childress, interior designer Mirza Dickel, craft-gallery owner JoAnn Rapp, and consultant for architectural crafts Bridget McCarthy. For those craftsmen juried in, the black-and-white photographs and the pertinent information that they sent were used to compile this catalog.

Not every craftsman working in architectural projects in Washington, Oregon, Idaho, Montana, Colorado, Wyoming, Utah, Nevada, Arizona, and New Mexico is included here. Some heard about the project too late. Some work in isolation and were not known to the Foundation, state arts agencies, or other organizations. Others were out of the country or couldn't provide usable photographs. This book is just the beginning, and it is hoped that architects, interior designers, and others in the market for architecturally integrated crafts will not stop here in their search to find the right craftsman for the right project.

A craftsman tends to be master of a particular medium, and within that material can produce a wide range of objects. Woodworkers can make doors, bannisters, chairs, and lamps, depending on their inclination. Some are also skilled at constructing walls, building decks, and doing fine cabinetry. Rarely, however, does a craftsman specialize in a particular *object* — lamps, for example — and then produce them in clay, wood, and metal. As a result, it was difficult to classify craftsmen and their work strictly in terms of products or building parts; that would have required a separate page for each kind of object craftsmen produce. A potter who makes sinks, tiles, and lamps, if classified according to the objects he makes, would have been listed in three separate sections of the catalog. Hence the following pages are organized for the most part by the *medium* in which each craftsman works, and at the bottom of the page is a short list of other kinds of things the craftsman makes. For additional information, there is also an index.

As a result of this specializing in one medium, craftsmen generally are able to do custom work that is not restricted to what is pictured in the following pages. The potter making lamps also probably makes, in a similar style, a wide variety of related ceramic products such as ornamental vases, bowls, or tableware. Thus, throughout the pages, style is the key element. A reader can feel fairly confident that if he is struck with the work of a particular craftsman, that craftsman would be able to do custom work in the style shown and produce just about anything in his medium. In shopping here, one is not buying off a shelf but, rather, hiring a skilled craftsman to do a custom job that would be unattainable elsewhere. Featured here are but a few examples of what is possible.

CHANSON CHING

213 West Cottonwood Street, Bozeman, MT 59715   (406) 586-2858

professional background

Ching has been making ceramics for many years and has exhibited widely.

business practices

Quantity pricing on 10 or more sinks; no minimum. Deposit required. No returns or cancellations. No warranty. No installation. Will ship for a fee. Flexible about color and scale of work.

other work

Made-to-order stoneware: tiles, urns, bird baths, and other items.

Here the client had two requests: that the faucets go through the rim of the sink and the glaze be made from local materials —in this case, clay from a nearby mountain.

At the request of his client, a fisherman, Ching decorated this sink with a brook trout and a rainbow trout.

CARL CHRISTENSEN

PO Box 355, Tome, NM 87060 (505) 865-4070

professional background
Christensen is a former instructor of English at East Texas State University.

business practices
Priced at $4 per 4¼-inch tile in a panel; no quantity pricing; no minimum. Deposit required. Returns and cancellations accepted. Credits given. Warranty. Will install or ship for a fee. Wide range of colors in ceramic glaze.

other work
Films.

Tile panel. Produced on speculation, now installed by the door of a house. The tiles create the design of a light cross on a dark field.

Close-up of the tile panel.

DAVID FERNANDEZ

275 Parkview Drive, Summit Park, UT 84060   (801) 649-9249
Kimball Art Center, PO Box 1478, Park City, UT 84060   (801) 649-8882

professional background
Since 1977, Fernandez has been the director of Kimball Art Center, Park City, Utah.

business practices
Priced from $100 to $175. Discount for 10 or more. No minimum. Deposit required. No returns. Cancellations accepted. Warranty. Plumber can install. Will ship for a fee. The desired diameter may be specified.

other work
Decorative ceramic pieces: floor bases, light fixtures, ceramic tables, and other items.

Fernandez produces basins for many contractors, designers, and architects. He uses five basic colors: blue, off-white, light green, tan-orange, and rust-black.

JIM FOSTER

10315 North County Road 15 Waverly, Fort Collins, CO 80524   (303) 568-7768
Lutz Bergerson Gallery, South Santa Fe Road, PO Box 1674, Taos, NM 87571   (505) 758-9734

professional background
Foster has taught at a number of universities and has exhibited widely.

business practices
Prices negotiated each time. Quantity pricing available; no minimum. Deposit required. No returns or cancellations. Warranty. Will install. Very flexible about specific requirements.

other work
Free-standing large metal and ceramic sculpture; basins.

Ceramic mural, 20 by 4 feet.

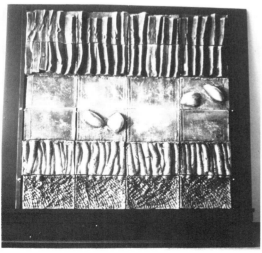

Ceramic mural, 84 by 84 inches. Foster's murals are in clay, wood, and bronze. He considers the personal tastes and interests of clients very important to the design of his murals, which tend toward earth colors, although he uses bright colors too. His flat murals look more like paintings than the murals shown.

WILLIAM T. GILBERT

Box 123, Cerrillos, NM 87010   (505) 471-3246

professional background
Since 1975, Gilbert has given work-shops, lectures, and demonstrations throughout the West. He has exhibited nationally.

business practices
Quantity pricing for over 500 square feet; otherwise, $8 to $10 per square foot; no minimum. No returns. No cancellations. Warranty if Gilbert installs. Will install or ship for a fee. Six colors in stock.

other work
Pottery, sculpture, and tile murals.

Tile floor. Gilbert's floors have soft, subtle variations in the intensity of the color of the tiles. They provide an unobtrusive yet pleasing background for any tiled areas including bathrooms, saunas, decks, and dining rooms.

BARBARA GRYGUTIS

273 North Main Street, Tucson, AZ 85705 (602) 622-5214

professional background
Grygutis's work has appeared in many magazines, and she has received many grants and awards for her work.

business practices
Roughly $30 to $100 per square foot. Deposit required. No returns. No cancellations. Warranty. Shipping and installation included. Flexible about color, finish, and other specifications.

other work
Ceramic sculpture.

Fountain for Cochise College, Sierra Vista, Arizona, four monoliths, 4 to 6 inches high. After completion of the pool, the architect decided to include a fountain, and hired Grygutis. The fountain, which reflects the landscape around the college, has a rather amorphous shape to contrast with the clean lines of the building.

Detail of the spillway.

Tile mural and spillway for pool and spa, Tucson, private house. Both the owner and the architect wanted artwork incorporated into the pool and spa. Grygutis proposed putting a mural on the back wall of the pool and then having a row of tiles relating to the mural emerge from the pool and making a continuous band around the spa.

VICKI HALPER

930 West 10th Avenue, Eugene, OR 97402 (503) 343-2948

professional background

Halper has done all but her dissertation to complete a Ph.D. from the University of Pennsylvania. She has been doing her tiles for many years.

business practices

Priced from $20 to $60 per square foot. No quantity pricing; $100 minimum order. Deposit: 25 percent. No returns. Tile setter should install. Will ship for a fee. Wide range of colors.

other work

Bathroom basins and mounted ceramic wall hangings.

SWAN MOSSBERG

Fireplace and hearth. In doing this project for her own home, Halper says she learned much about the need to persist on a project until those who will live with the work are totally happy.

SWAN MOSSBERG

Iris tiled bathroom (detail). The clients knew Halper's work from local galleries and called her for the project. They took samples home, and Halper visited them there. If unable to visit, Halper can use blueprints.

SWAN MOSSBERG

Tellers' screen, Bank of the Northwest, Eugene, Oregon (detail). An interior designer for whom Halper frequently works gave her this assignment. After a design was worked out, it was approved by bank officers. The tiles run the length of the screen and give people waiting something nice to look at.

NANCY JACQUOT

1072 Empinado Drive, Laramie, WY 82070   (307) 742-2785

professional background

Jacquot has been active in pottery for a number of years, and her work has been in many shows.

business practices

Priced from $100 to $200 per sink. No quantity pricing; no minimum. Deposit required. Will install or ship for a fee. Color, finish, and so forth, may be changed.

other work

Wall murals and tiles. Lamps. Soap dishes, toothbrush holders, and other items can be made to coordinate with sinks.

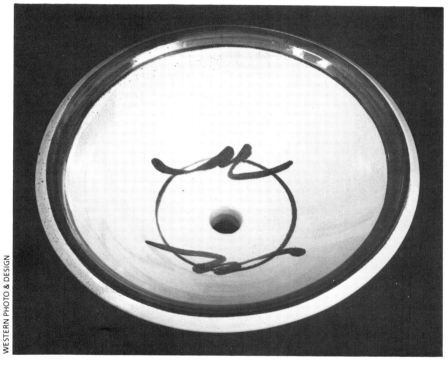

WESTERN PHOTO & DESIGN

WESTERN PHOTO & DESIGN

Sinks. Jacquot likes to have clients discuss colors and sizes for sinks, and then she will do what is agreed upon. She does a variety of designs, but prefers those that are simple.

ALLAN KLUBER

243 West D Street, Springfield, OR 97477   (503) 747-0950

professional background
Kluber exhibits nationally and has received several large public commissions.

business practices
Priced from $25 to $40 per square foot. No quantity pricing; no minimum. Deposit required. No returns. No cancellations. Warranty. Tile setter should install. Will ship by UPS for a fee. Various colors, thicknesses, and finishes.

other work
Illuminated clay: translucent clay that's a transition between normal clay and glass.

Porcelain colored clay tile for hot-pot surface adjacent to kitchen range. Client was familiar with Kluber's work. They discussed preferences and agreed upon an adaptation.

Waterproof sanitary wall surrounding kitchen sink area. Kluber reviewed his past work with the client, and a general design was agreed upon. Porcelain tiles with plants impressed into them were installed.

Porcelain tile for fireplace hearth and opening. Some tiles are plant impressed; floor tiles are plain. An architect referred clients to Kluber.

MICK LAMONT & BARBARA JENSEN-LAMONT

Route 2, Box 302 B, Portland, OR 97231 (503) 621-3487

professional background
The Lamonts have worked together for a number of years. Their work is shown widely and is found in many collections.

business practices
Quantity pricing available; otherwise, $40 to $50 per square foot for tiles; minimum order of $500. Deposit required. Warranty. Tile setter should install. Will ship by UPS for a fee. Flexible about color and other specifications.

other work
Lamps, functional stoneware, and porcelain.

Fireplace surroundings and hearth in the home of a husband and wife architect and interior designer team. They were active participants in the design process, which included several meetings, a scale drawing, and a full-scale cartoon.

Fireplace wall mural. The clients in this new house left the space blank while looking for the right design solution. After three years they came across the Lamonts' work, and the design process went quickly.

Sinks and counter at the Oregon School of Arts and Crafts. During the design process, the Lamonts met with a building committee and presented a proposal, then held various meetings to discuss details. The committee reviewed the work in progress.

JOAN LINCOLN

6821 Lost Dutchman Drive, Paradise Valley, AZ 85253   (602) 948-5813

professional background
Lincoln has been working in clay for many years, and has done many major installations.

business practices
Priced at $100 per square foot; no quantity pricing; no minimum. Deposit required. No returns. Cancellations accepted. Warranty. Will install or deliver for a fee. Flexible about designs. Delivery time: three to four months.

other work
Floor coverings, signage and graphics, and kitchen and bathroom tiles.

Fountain at the Town Mall, Paradise Valley. Many other craftsmen had their designs rejected before Lincoln submitted hers and had it accepted by the town council. She submitted a model, materials samples, a cost sheet, and a time line, and was given a contract and a 33⅓ percent advance payment. The fountain was finished two weeks ahead of time and 98¢ under budget.

Detail of fountain.

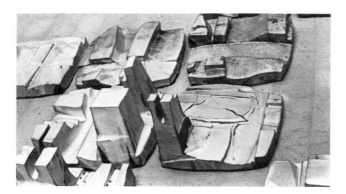

Detail of installation at Western Savings Bank showing three-dimensional possibilities of tiles. The piece was purchased by an architect for the building which was then under construction. Lincoln originally did it as part of her master's thesis.

N. SKREKO MARTIN

902 East Hampton Street, Tucson, AZ 85719   (602) 622-1506

professional background

Martin has been in many national publications, and has had a number of architectural commissions and grants.

business practices

Quantity pricing available; otherwise, minimum of $35 per square foot; minimum order of $200. Deposit required. No returns or cancellations. Warranty. Will ship and install for a fee. Flexible about color and finish.

other work

Fountains, planters, game boards, free-standing sculpture, signs, and other items.

Remodeled kitchen counter. The tile counter conforms to the handmade character of the house and can withstand use by teenage cooks.

Outdoor tile mural. Martin worked with another artist, a painter, to produce this design in tile. She will consider future joint efforts with artists whose work she respects.

Detail of counter.

JOYCE NEWMAN

1517 South Dexter Way, Denver, CO 80222   (303) 757-2143

professional background
Newman, who has a Ph.D. in bio-chemistry, has exhibited widely, especially in Colorado.

business practices
Priced from $75 to $150 per square foot. No quantity pricing; no minimum. Deposit required. No returns or cancellations. War-ranty. Installation included. Will ship for a fee. Thickness, color, and finish variable.

other work
Free-standing sculpture.

Town Meeting. *Littleton, Colorado, Civic Center; 33 feet long. After being chosen for the project, Newman submitted drawings and a ceramic model. She made monthly reports to the architect, and kept in close contact.*

Gathering. *University of Northern Colorado, Greeley, Colo-rado. This work, a group of 40 ceramic figures installed on a balcony facing, was chosen in competition under the Art in Public Places Law. Newman worked very closely with the architect at every stage. The work inspires interest and excite-ment without being busy.*

Detail of Gathering.

JEANNE OTIS

1433 East Wesleyan Drive, Tempe, AZ 85282   (602) 965-7285 (work) or 839-3873 (studio)

professional background

Otis, an assistant professor at Arizona State University, has exhibited nationally.

business practices

Priced at $100 per square foot; no quantity pricing; minimum of $500. Deposit required. No returns. Cancellations accepted. Warranty. Will install for a fee. Will ship free. Glazed or un- glazed, variety of colors. Delivery time eight weeks for 16 pieces.

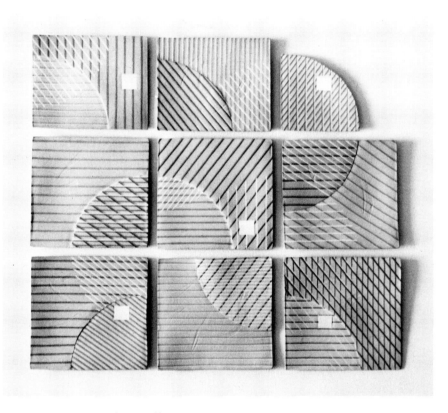

Falling Timbers. *Porcelain wall piece. Each major unit measures 15½ inches on each side. The clay slabs —decorated with underglaze pencil drawings that suggest fabric patterns —are fired to high temperatures, re-sulting in surfaces with only 2 percent porosity.*

Fool's Puzzle. *Porcelain wall piece. Otis generally first submits a study painting to the client. With an opaque projector, the painting can be projected on the wall to actual size. Later, the client is asked to approve glazed color samples before the piece is started.*

RALPH PARDINGTON

Ralph and Joyce Ltd., 129 West San Francisco Street, Box 751, Santa Fe, NM 87501 (505) 982-9303

professional background
Pardington has been in many shows and received many awards. He has a great deal of experience both as an administrator and as a practicing craftsman.

business practices
Quantity pricing available. No minimum. Deposit required. Returns accepted. Will install for a fee. Will ship C.O.D. Some flexibility about color and finish.

other work
Fountain sculpture and functional pottery.

The design for this sink and counter came from several conversations with the architect, contractor, and client. The sink is oval, 18 inches in length.

Sunken tub. Pardington was told where the tub would go, and worked within the limitations of the space in consultation with the client.

WILLIAM RICHARDS

149 NE 53rd, Seattle, WA 98105   (206) 633-5446

professional background
Richards received his M.F.A. degree from the University of Washington in 1981 and has exhibited widely in ceramics for the past three years.

business practices
Priced from $300 to $600 for each plate 18 to 26 inches in diameter. No quantity pricing; no minimum order. Anyone can install. Will ship for a fee. General ideas, colors, and details can be worked out to meet the client's needs. Plates are treated with a surface sealer.

other work
Clay sculpture.

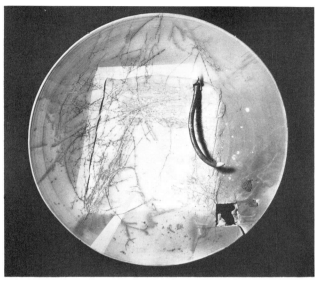

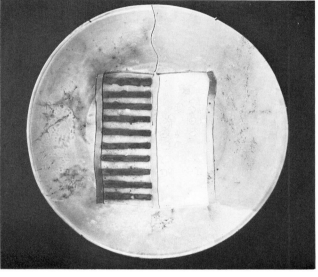

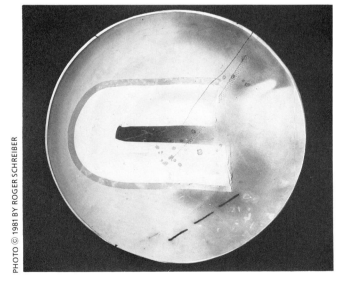

Three ceramic plates, each about 21 to 22 inches in diameter. Colors are applied by hand or airbrush, and the pieces then are low-fired with salt. They come complete with hanging hardware.

SANDRA ROBISHAW

10695 Arapahoe Road, Lafayette, CO 80026   (303) 665-9623

professional background
Robishaw has a background in graphic design and now works full time in ceramics and sculpture.

business practices
Quantity pricing available; otherwise, $40 to $60 per square foot for ceramic wall pieces. Concrete pieces priced according to design. Minimum order required. Deposit required. No returns or cancellations. Warranty. Installation included generally. Concrete can have color added. Ceramic color and other specifications can vary too.

other work
Sculpture and concrete forms.

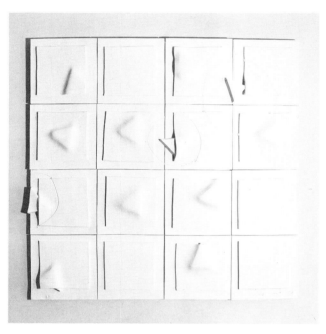

Terra cotta tile wall installation. The client wanted a wall installation for a sunny breakfast nook. Robishaw created a design which would change with the sunlight and be enhanced by it. She designed two tiles; one flat, and one with diagonal raised ridges to create shadows, and placed them in various patterns on the wall. The clay is in warm, subtle hues. The client approved an original sketch and then the final pattern at the time of installation.

Ceramic tile wall piece. The tiles range in color from white to buff. They are sculpted in relief and mounted on Plexiglas. The shadows vary with the light in the room.

CAROLYN SALE

Route 5, Box 308, Los Lunas, NM 87031   (505) 865-5924

professional background
Sale has exhibited her work for over 10 years, both in the Southwest and the Northeast.

business practices
Quantity pricing available; otherwise, $18 to $30 per square foot; no minimum. Deposit required. No returns. Deposit not refunded with cancellations. Warranty. Tile setter should install. Will ship for a fee. Flexible about color and finish.

other work
Interior and exterior tiles: doors, countertops, street numbers, and others.

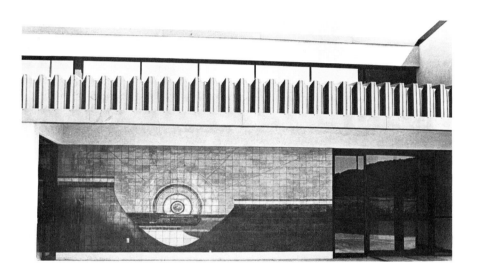

All of Sale's work is custom designed. For each job she works with the architect, designer, contractor, or client to come up with the right design for the environment. She can work on distant projects from descriptions, photographs, and samples of the local materials.

Tile mural at Laguna Pueblo. For this project she worked with the architect and visited with the Laguna people. The Pueblo Council approved the design.

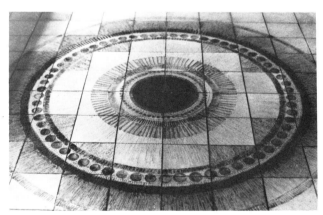

Floor tiles. Sale worked with the architect and the client. The architectural emphasis in the building is on sunlit spaces. The design conformed with bright, radiating colors.

Fireplace and banco tiles. Here Sale worked directly with the owners. Other colors in the room influenced selection of the colors of the tiles.

GEORGIA SARTORIS

4851 South Forest Hill Road, Evergreen, CO 80439   (303) 674-6195

professional background
Sartoris has been an independent studio potter and sculptor since 1971. She has had many shows and won many awards.

business practices
Quantity pricing available; otherwise, about $50 per square foot; no minimum. Deposit required. Returns accepted. Warranty. Will install or ship for a fee.

other work
Single and modular groups of wall-mounted ceramic sculpture, large earthenware plates, and large sculptural vessels.

Wall group produced on speculation. This piece illustrates Sartoris's interest in repetition of organic shapes. It could be arranged in many different shapes or expanded to suit the space available. Sartoris believes design should generally come from interaction with the client. She likes to do one-of-a-kind projects.

Sculptural grouping of tiles designed to complement a high vaulted ceiling in a contemporary house. Designed by the craftsman. The earthenware was organically fired.

ANNE STORRS

1514 SE Tolman, Portland, OR 97202   (503) 232-9039

professional background

Storrs has been making tiles for
five years. She has installations
in many public and private buildings in Oregon.

business practices

Priced at $60 per square foot plus
design time; no quantity pricing;
no minimum. Will install, or a
tile setter can. Will ship for a fee.
A range of colors.

BILL BACHHUBER

*Western Forestry Center, Portland.
For these tiles in an outside concrete
wall which served as a bench back,
Storrs worked with the Forestry Center
director. One of Storrs's ideas was to
follow the state tree, the Douglas fir,
through its life cycle. The director
suggested color, tests were made, and
production began.*

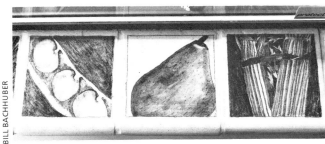

BILL BACHHUBER

*Window ledge, Oregon School of Arts and Crafts (detail).
Storrs presented her ideas for this ledge to a panel, and the
panel approved them.*

BILL BACHHUBER

*Kitchen, private house. The client went to the studio and liked
a series of round things Storrs displayed there. For the kitchen,
61 tiles of round objects were used. Storrs likes her clients to
be familiar with her work, and she likes to know them before
working out a design with them.*

ANNE VERALDI

3502 Meridian Avenue North, Seattle, WA 98103   (206) 633-5232

professional background
Veraldi works full time in ceramics.

business practices
Quantity pricing available; no minimum. Returns accepted. No cancellations. Warranty. Tile setter should install. Will ship by UPS for a fee. Color, finish, and other specifications can vary.

other work
Ceramic sculpture.

Veraldi makes ceramic animal images to be mounted on walls. The difficulty of working with clay on larger forms has limited her to the wall pieces. She is happy to work with clients on a theme, size of pieces, and other decisions.

JUDITH WILLIAMS
505 West 10th Street, Pueblo, CO 81003   (303) 542-1032

professional background
Williams has worked with ceramics for over 10 years, and has had many commissions.

business practices
Quantity pricing available; otherwise, $10 to $20 per square foot; no minimum. Will ship or install for a fee. Tile setter can install.

other work
Lamps pierced with internal lights, candle lanterns for restaurants, and garden sculpture.

Ekos House. Williams was commissioned by the architects to design and manufacture a suitable decoration for the border of this entire building. The cost was established before work began. The tiles were placed in an existing groove.

Colorado School District 60, president's office. Williams was commissioned by the architects to design and manufacture this ceramic tile for the base of the room and doors. Budget established by architects after approval of samples.

Detail of a commemorative plaque for past presidents of an art center. The tiles were installed by the craftsman.

DEANNA LEE BIRKHOLM

Classic Glass, Wilsall, MT 59086   (406) 686-4694

professional background
Birkholm spent years researching methods of getting consistent, good results with etching.

business practices
Priced at 50¢ to 75¢ per square inch, single run; no quantity pricing; no minimum. No returns; cancellations accepted. Deposit required. No warranties. Installation should be done by a carpenter or a glazier. Will ship for a fee.

other work
Acid-etched glass for kitchen cabinets, mirrors. Works on existing vertical surfaces without removing them.

Sheraton Hotel, Billings. Birkholm restored the doors with existing stained glass from the Babcock Opera House (circa 1890). Design was left to the artist after she had inspected the doors and the rooms they would serve. She worked closely with the owner/architect.

Private house, with etched glass for main door. The owners left the design to the artist, who kept in mind the log construction and country setting.

ED CARPENTER
3125 Van Waters, Milwaukie, OR 97222   (503) 653-5230

professional background
Carpenter has studied with Lud-
wig Schaffrath in West Germany,
has written many articles for
national publications, and has
received numerous grants and
awards for his work.

business practices
Business details specified in the
contract.

*North-facing breezeway window at the Oregon School of Arts
and Crafts, Portland. The window measures 8 feet by 8½ feet
and was designed and executed by Carpenter, who wanted it to
be like a big uneven lens through which a viewer could see the
changes in the north sky.*

*Interior screen at Omark Industries Saw Chain Division
Headquarters, Portland. Designed by Carpenter and executed
by Tim O'Neill, the screen measures 9 by 17 feet and was
intended to be a simple, ornamental, light-transmitting wall
that would separate the executive offices from the stair well.
Omark manufactures approximately 85 percent of the world's
chainsaw chains.*

GARTH EDWARDS

3410 SW Water Street, Portland, OR 97201 (503) 223-5012

professional background

Edwards has had numerous commissions in the Northwest and has recently been awarded an NEA Crafts Fellowship.

business practices

Priced at $125 per square foot; no quantity pricing; no minimum. Deposit required. No returns. Installation and shipping included, as in contract.

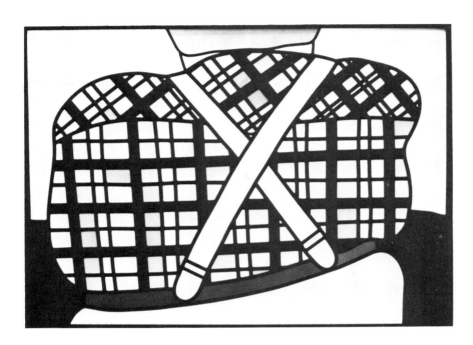

Logger Back. *Edwards sketched the basic design for this work while watching a logger wolf down hot cakes at a truck stop.*

Socialite. *Edwards's gentle humor is evident in all his people pieces.*

Mad. *This piece, like the others, is made with German antique glass.*

MARK ERIC GULSRUD

10213 Peacock Hill Avenue, Gig Harbor, WA 98335 (206) 858-3236

professional background
Gulsrud is a self-employed studio artist who works with glass and clay.

business practices
Priced from $50 to $100 per square foot. No quantity pricing; no minimum. Deposit and warranty. No returns or cancellations. Installation often included in price. Windows are weather tight. Plate-glass backing is recommended where windows are vulnerable.

other work
Room dividers with leaded glass and clay relief. Clay architectural accent pieces: pots to murals.

Window in private house, Santa Monica, California. Six feet high, the window is made from European handblown glasses, is leaded, and is reinforced internally with zinc came. A great deal of freedom accompanied the commission, the only stipulations being cool colors and an organic feel.

Gothic triptych window, Lutheran Church, Los Angeles, 9 feet high. Gulsrud worked with the pastor and the church council, whose ideas progressed from stereotypical figures for the windows to abstract compositions. Once aware of more contemporary work, the congregation was very supportive.

DOUGLAS HANSEN

702 West Bertona Avenue, Seattle, WA 98119   (206) 282-9950

professional background

Hansen founded Glass Graphics in 1976. His work has appeared in numerous publications, and he has had many local commissions.

business practices

Quantity pricing available; otherwise, $75 to $100 per square foot; no minimum. No returns or cancellations. Deposit required. Warranty. Installation available. Will ship. Finished in black, copper, or brass and zinc.

other work

Sculpture lighting, tapestry, and environmental art.

PHOTO © 1981 BY ROGER SCHREIBER

Entrance doors, Holy Rosary Church, Edmonds, Washington. The design was worked out in a series of meetings with the architects. Opaque glass was used to create a screen effect but without color so as not to compete with the main altar windows. Square shapes were used to pick up the dominant square interior tiling of the church.

PHOTO © 1981 BY ROGER SCHREIBER

Glass entrance panels, Gig Harbor High School, Gig Harbor, Washington. This commission was obtained through juried competition. A large mass of clear glass was needed because there were no other windows in the building. The lines of the piece emphasize the school motto, "the tides."

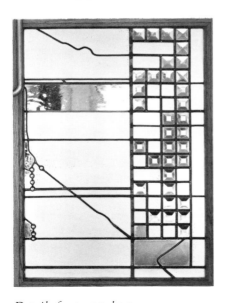

Detail of entrance doors.

FREDERICK HEIDEL

932 NW Summit Avenue, Portland, OR 97210 (503) 226-1131
% Fountain Gallery, 117 NW 21st Street, Portland, OR 97209 (503) 228-8476

professional background
Heidel has an M.F.A. degree from the Art Institute of Chicago. He was Professor of Art, Portland State University, from 1951 to 1980, and Chairman of the Department of Art and Architecture from 1951 to 1977.

business practices
Priced from $200 to $250 per square foot. Less on large pieces. No minimum; no returns; credits. Deposit required. Warranty. Will ship and install for a fee. Will repair at no cost within six months of installation if the damage is the fault of the craftsman. Delivery time three to six months.

other work
Laminated glass sculpture.

Landau Chapel, Temple Beth Israel Cemetary, Portland. Each panel is 5 by 6 feet, 330 square feet in all. Panels are resin laminated stained glass on ⅜-inch-thick tempered plate glass.

Sparks Memorial Chapel, Holiday Park Hospital. Each panel is 74 by 9 inches of resin laminated stained glass on two sides of ¼-inch-thick tempered plate glass.

MICHAEL KENNEDY

308 34th Avenue East, Seattle, WA 98112   (206) 329-1837

professional background

Kennedy shows and lectures widely in the Seattle area. He started the glass program at Bellevue Community College.

business practices

Priced from $300. Deposit required. No returns or cancellations. Warranty. Installation included. Will ship for a fee.

Window, 8 by 14 feet, in Federal Way, Washington, District Courthouse, done for the King County Arts Commission's percent-for-arts program. Kennedy worked with already existing architectural plans, softening the lines of the building design.

PAUL MARIONI

4136 Meridian Avenue North, Seattle, WA 98103 (206) 633-1901

professional background

Marioni's work has appeared in many national glass shows and in *Artweek, Vogue, Glass Art, Time,* and other magazines. He was given an NEA fellowship in 1975 and taught at Pilchuck from 1974 to 1980. He has a U.S. patent on his process for working specific imagery into molten glass.

business practices

Price depends on project; quantity pricing available; no minimum. Deposit. Returns, credits, cancellations. One-year warranty. Installation free if local; will ship free in U.S.A. Delivery time depends on size.

Delridge Community Center, Seattle. This 6-by-13-inch window was a percent-for-art project. Marioni worked with the architect from the beginning of the project to develop a suitable space. The glass was cast in molds designed by Marioni to make cast glass feasible for architectural use. The building houses the state boxing program.

MARK SULLO

The Premonition. This 22-by-28-inch panel is displayed in a light box to read well in any environment. The panel is owned by Marioni.

HOWARD MEEHAN

368 NW Lomita, Portland, OR 97210   (503) 222-0096 (home) or 627-1760 (work)

professional background
Meehan, with a design background, has taught both in the United States and Japan, has exhibited nationally, and owns several patents.

business practices
Priced from $80 to $100 per square foot. No quantity pricing; no minimum. Deposit required. Returns and cancellations accepted. Credit given. Warranty. Installation and shipping included, as stated in contract.

other work
Architectural glass brick, sandblasted and sculptured.

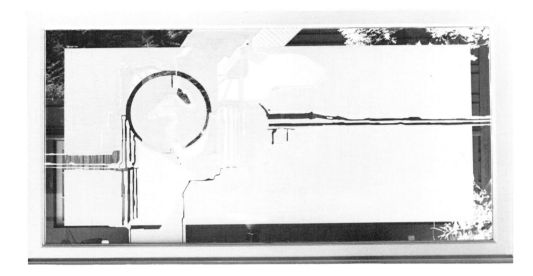

Window, private house. This glass is sculptural with sandblasted deep relief on both sides. Meehan is capable of working much larger, up to 8-by-10-foot, panels.

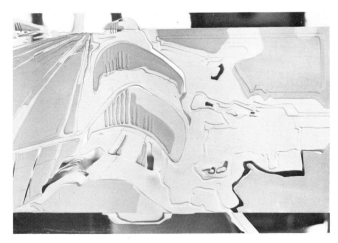

Detail of room divider panel.

Panel for room divider in a Portland restaurant. The design for this rather abstract piece was inspired by shellfish.

RICHARD POSNER

1314 Denny Way, Seattle, WA 98109   (206) 624-3341

professional background
Posner has been a visiting crafts-man at many noted schools, has received many awards, and currently is working on two books.

business practices
Quantity pricing available; otherwise, $150 to $500 per square foot; no minimum. Cancellations accepted. Warranty. Will install or ship for a fee. No refunds once work on the project has begun.

other work
Sculpture, films, drawings, books.

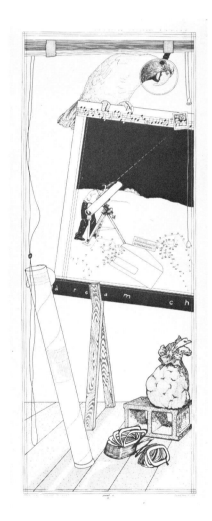

Another Look at My Beef with the Government. *This work shows the craftsman in traction and looking through the window, with various beefs scattered around the room, which* *refer to Posner's history as a conscientious objector. Posner delights in taking an idea and creating humorous imagery for it.*

Dream Chartres of Four Gone Conclusions, *first of four panels, the Exploratorium, San Francisco. For these windows in the science museum, Posner was told the panels should somehow complement the scientific displays on the floor. They should also be 50 percent clear glass to allow daydreamers to look outside.*

LAURIE L. THAL

Star Route 352 A, Jackson, WY 83001   (307) 733-5096
Artwest, Box 1248, Jackson, WY 83001   (307) 733-6379

professional background
Thal has been working with glass since the mid-seventies, and she has been in various shows nationwide.

business practices
No quantity pricing. Deposit required. Will install or ship. Flexible about color, size, and other specifications.

other work
Handblown functional and nonfunctional forms.

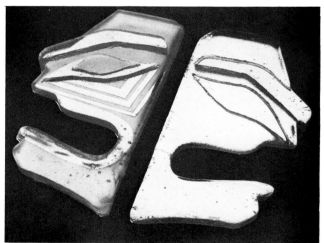

These solid glass masks, ranging in thickness from 1 to 3 inches, are cast in sand and are quite translucent although they could be made opaque. They could be used architecturally in walls, doors, or windows, or they could be used as tiles. The mask motif is experimental for Thal, who sees possible future uses including fountains and gargoyles. Commissioned work would be influenced by the environment and the ideas and feelings of the client.

CANDYCE ANDERSON

4603 North Cheyenne Street, Tacoma, WA 98407 (206) 752-3456

professional background
Anderson currently is an art instructor at Charles Wright Academy, Tacoma. She exhibits widely throughout the Northwest.

business practices
Priced from $110 to $150. For six or more, 35 percent off retail. Returns and credits for exchanges only. Deposit 25 percent. No cancellations. No warranty. Will ship by UPS for a fee.

other work
Planters, wall pouches for fresh and dried flowers and other items, and soap dishes.

Lamp, unglazed clay that gives an earthy quality that goes well with the casual style of contemporary living. The clay resembles fabric or leather, getting its surface texture from the canvas on which the craftsman makes the slabs of clay. This lamp is 22 inches high including the shade.

Lamp 29 inches high including shade.

Detail showing relief in porcelain.

FRANK BOYDEN

Route 2, Box 17, Otis, OR 97368   (503) 994-5198

professional background
Boyden has an M.F.A. degree from Yale, exhibits nationally, and has operated his pottery on the Oregon coast since 1972. He has been making lamps for five years.

business practices
No quantity pricing; no minimum. No returns. Deposit required. Warranty. Will ship by UPS for a fee of $25 per piece.

other work
Steel/ceramic wall pieces. Heat-exchange systems for ceramic kilns.

Three lamps. Boyden makes 30 percent of his lamps on commission, mainly for finished interiors. Shades may be chosen by the craftsman or by the client. The rigging is the best avail- *able: solid brass, when possible, and three-way switches, all rigged by a lamp company, and all approved by the Underwriters Laboratory.*

GOODWIN HARDING

GLENN BURRIS

36838 Jefferson-Scio Drive, Jefferson, OR 97352   (503) 394-3222

professional background

Burris has an M.F.A. degree from the University of Iowa, and has been a self-supporting studio potter for eight years.

business practices

Priced from $60 to $200. No quantity pricing; no minimum. Cancellations and returns accepted. No deposit. No warranty. Will ship for additional 10 percent (approximately). About eight weeks delivery time.

other work

Decorative and functional ceramics including vases, ginger jars, dinnerware, teapots, and other items.

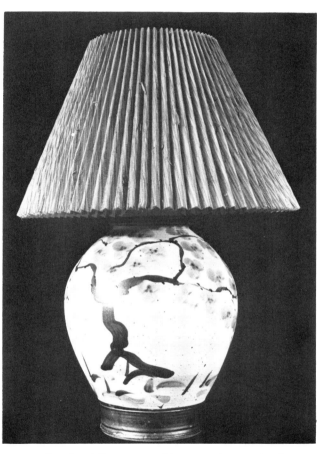

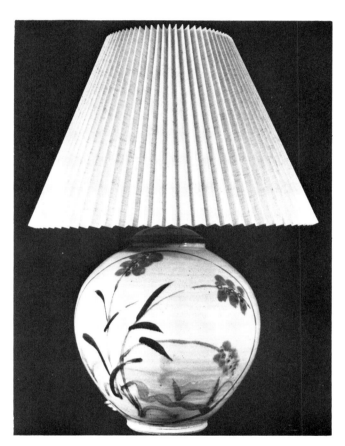

Burris offers five different sizes of lamps and can assist the decorator or client in choosing the right size for a particular setting, as well as the right surface and color. This lamp is a dry white matte with decorations in brown and turquoise.

Lamp with celadon green glaze with brushwork in brown, muted blue, and a touch of pink.

KENNETH EMERSON

3205 395th North, Carson City, NV 89701   (702) 849-0627

professional background

Emerson has a degree in architecture and frequently works with architects.

business practices

Quantity pricing available; no minimum. Deposit required. Returns accepted; no cancellations. Warranty. Will install or ship when specified in contract. Oil finish or others.

other work

All types of woodworking: desks, counters, and cabinetry.

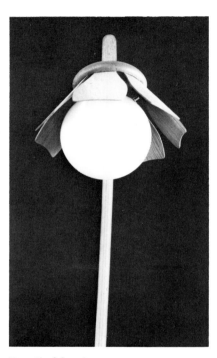

Detail of floor lamp.

Floor lamp. This whimsical piece was conceived for a room with lots of plants and windows. Made of oak (chosen for its bendability and informality), it is finished in oil to let all the grain show.

DAVID FERNANDEZ

275 Parkview Drive, Summit Park, UT 84060   (801) 649-9249
Kimball Art Center, PO Box 1478, Park City, UT 84060   (801) 649-8882

professional background
Since 1977, Fernandez has been the director of Kimball Art Center, Park City, Utah.

business practices
Quantity pricing available; otherwise, $30 to $500; no minimum. Deposit required. No returns. Cancellations accepted. Warranty. An electrician can install. Will ship for a fee. Delivery time four weeks for up to 10 pieces; six weeks for more.

other work
Variety of decorative ceramic pieces: floor vases, sinks, ceramic tables, and other items.

Hanging fixture. This piece was designed to be the focal point of the dining room of this home. The basic design here too can be adapted to specific needs.

Outdoor light fixture designed to withstand severe mountain weather. The body of the fixture is wheel-thrown stoneware which houses a brass holder. The glass globe is handblown. The basic fixture can be modified for specific situations.

ALLAN KLUBER

243 West D Street, Springfield, OR 97477 (503) 747-0950

professional background
In 1981, Kluber won an NEA Building Arts Grant for the further development of illuminated clay for use in architectural crafts. His treatment of clay yields a transitional material between ordinary clay and glass.

business practices
No quantity pricing; no minimum. No returns or cancellations. Deposit required. Warranty. Will ship by UPS for 15 percent of price. Delivery time: one to three months.

other work
Tiles.

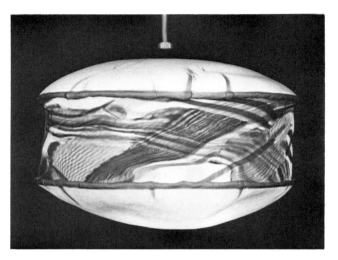

This hanging globe was purchased from a gallery show for an intimate dining area.

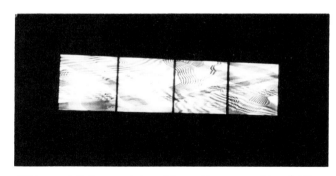

This panel light was designed for a client to provide soft illumination in a dark corner. It is visually exciting even when the light is off.

All three pieces are made from what Kluber calls "illuminated clay," the result of a new ceramic process that offers an unlimited range of color hue and intensity and considerable flexibility in shape and design. The light is warm, soft, and inviting. This chandelier was designed for a high ceiling in the home of a client.

MARK PRATT

Pratt Designs, 5508 SW Cameron Road, Portland, OR 97221 (503) 245-5795

professional background
An interest in interior lighting projects led Pratt to his lighting design business.

business practices
Priced at $80 and up; discount of 10 percent on 10 or more of the same design; no minimum. Deposit required. No returns or cancellations. Warranty. Will ship by UPS for a fee. Finishes of paint, nickel, brass, and chrome (satin or full-gloss). Custom finishes and colors for large orders.

other work
Lighting fixtures of all kinds.

Probe Nautilus. This fixture in the Nautilus series has a light which can be turned in all directions by using the protruding handles to manipulate the head shell. The fixture includes a full-range dimmer control and a power cord that can be arranged to add to the decor.

Pratt Nautilus, the table-top lamp in the Nautilus series. The shade diffuses light outward while casting direct light downward. The lamp has a dimmer control. Pratt here sought clean lines with an organic feeling.

JOHN ROGERS

1530 SE Holly Street, Portland, OR 97214   (503) 239-4181 or 653-5230

professional background
Rogers has been working in ceramics for about 10 years and has had a number of large commissions.

business practices
Generally $120 per square foot. Includes installation. No quantity pricing. No returns or cancellations. Deposit required. Warranty. Shipping included. Delivery time depends on size. Flexible about colors and other specifications.

other work
Ceramic surfaces for buildings; small porcelain shapes.

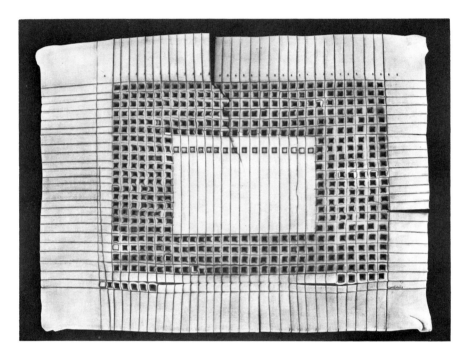

Porcelain light fixture, 18 inches in diameter. Concave-mounted with soft white glass globe behind and soft, subtle surfaces. Rheostat control.

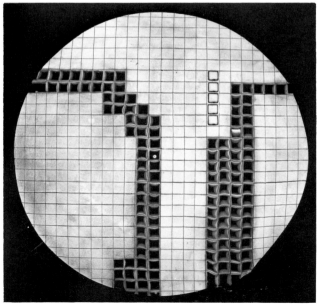

Porcelain light fixture, 18 inches in diameter. Concave-mounted with soft white glass globe behind and soft, subtle surfaces. Rheostat control.

PAUL VON ROSENSTIEL

603 Lake Washington Boulevard East, Seattle, WA 98112   (206) 328-1725

professional background

Von Rosenstiel is a self-employed designer/builder with a special interest in custom woodworking and solar energy. He has degrees in architecture from Columbia and the University of Washington.

business practices

No quantity pricing; no minimum; no returns. Deposit required. Cancellations accepted. Warranty. Price of installation depends on location. Will ship for a fee. Delivery time depends on piece.

other work

Solar energy work, renovations, and hardware.

Alcove reading light. Fluorescent strip lamp covered by fir slats. The light is integrated with a skylight to allow for both natural and artificial lighting of the area.

Entry wall light of coiled soft copper pipe on a turned red oak plate with an incandescent spotlight. The spotlight was chosen to highlight artwork on the adjacent wall. The copper, red oak, and incandescent bulb all help create a sense of warmth.

This hanging lamp was designed and built for clients who wanted down-lighting on their dining table and some illumination for the whole room. They also wanted the lamp to be lightweight and graceful. It is made of oak veneer strips and a laminated walnut ring with a turned walnut top and cover plate.

TIMOTHY ZIKRATCH

406 North Eighth, Pocatello, ID 83201   (208) 232-2972
In The Woods, 322 East Whitman, Pocatello, ID 83201   (208) 233-4003

professional background
Zikratch began his custom wood business, In The Woods, in 1978. He works with individuals, architects, craftsmen, and contractors.

business practices
Quantity pricing available; no minimum. Returns and cancellations accepted, with 10 percent retained. Credits. Deposit required. Will ship for a fee. Delivery time: eight weeks.

other work
Almost anything with wood: store interiors, doors, car dashes, altars, stairways, and so forth.

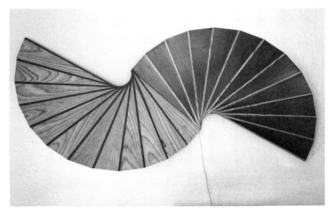

Light fixture, 30 by 70 inches. Made of ash and cherry, this fixture now lives in a private home.

Table lamp, 18 inches high, maple and black walnut. Produced on speculation.

Floor lamp, 72 inches high, made of oak and mahogany, laminated, bentwood construction. Owned by the craftsman.

ROBERT KARL BEHRENS

2505 West 36th Avenue, Denver, CO 80211 (303) 433-0793

professional background
Behrens has exhibited nationwide and has worked with architects in various major cities.

business practices
Pricing as in contract. Deposit required. No returns or cancellations. Warranty. Pieces built on the site.

other work
Walls, fountains, sculpture, and landscapes.

Shelters, Cherry Creek Recreation Area, Colorado. The architect who received the commission for the shelters asked Behrens to work with him. The final design shows Behrens's style. The shelters extend down the shoreline of the lake formed by the dammed-up creek. Behrens chose the locations for the pieces to create the desired overall impression. Since the shelters will occasionally be flooded, they had to be able to withstand water. Behrens built wood forms first, and the shelters were then made of reinforced concrete. They vaguely resemble the hulls of boats or the wings of seabirds.

MARGE HAMMOND-FARNESS

1155 NW 35th Street, Corvallis, OR 97330   (503) 752-7306

professional background

Hammond-Farness is a lifelong resident of Oregon. She is aware of her environment and wants her work to help other people pause and notice grace and beauty.

business practices

Quantity pricing available; otherwise, $200 to $5,000; no minimum. Deposit required. No returns or cancellations. Warranty. Will install or ship for a fee. Delivery time 3 to 12 months if not in studio inventory.

other work

Bird baths, bird houses, planters, wall and pool reliefs, water and sun sculpture, and other items.

Tree planters, Portland Plaza. These planters were commissioned by a landscape architect who specified the interior dimensions, but relegated total design responsibility to Hammond-Farness. The various sides relate to the sculptural content of the Plaza Tower and surrounding buildings.

Various pieces created for a show at Salishan Lodge, Oregon. These pieces were produced on speculation, but Hammond-Farness frequently works with the specific needs of clients. She wants her pieces to help create people places, encouraging viewers to become more aware of their environment.

Planter, Oregon Physician Service Building, Portland. This work was commissioned.

MOLLY MASON

309 Richmond Drive SE, Albuquerque, NM 87106   (505) 277-3211 (studio) or 256-7191 (home)

professional background
Mason teaches sculpture at the University of New Mexico and has exhibited nationally.

business practices
Priced from $2,000 to $12,000; no minimum. Deposits, returns, and so forth, depend on the contract. Variety of finishes: oiled, varnished, sealed metal, and ceramic tiles; very flexible about specifications.

other work
Stainless steel outdoor sculpture; masonry and tile walls.

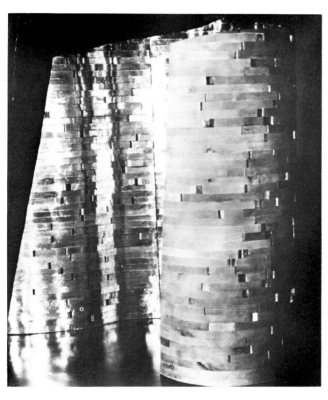

Firechamber, 85 inches high. The techniques used to build this work of alder and copper sheet could also be used to construct walls. Mason is currently doing an undulating 50-foot-long wall of tiles over concrete. She is working with the architect in charge of the percent-for-art project.

Madwoman's Garden. *Wood, steel, brass, copper, 87 inches high. This piece shows other possibilities for walls. Both pieces were produced on speculation.*

JUAN AND PATRICIA NAVARRETE

PO Box 2251, Taos, NM 87571   (505) 776-2942

professional background
Working together, Juan and Patricia build adobe fireplaces and renovate adobe homes and, also together, they run a museum established for the preservation of the Hispanic culture and art of the Southwest.

business practices
Price depends on size and sculpted embellishments. No quantity pricing; no minimum. Deposit required. No cancellations. Warranty. Fireplaces are built on location. Firebrick is used for the interior of the firebox. Building time is about two weeks.

other work
Wall and arch embellishments; films.

This fireplace also serves as a room divider. Design ideas went back and forth between the craftsmen and client. Natural earth colors were used. The left banco flanking the fireplace also has room for storing wood.

For this fireplace, the client requested art deco and Native American motifs, and helped to do some of the final embellishment.

RONALD PETTY

3720 Sunnyside Avenue North, Seattle, WA 98103   (206) 633-0876

professional background
In addition to doing sculptural concrete work, Petty has a general contracting business for custom-built houses.

business practices
Each project is priced individual-ly. After the initial mold is made, additional castings are made at a reduced rate. No minimum. Deposit required. No returns or cancellations. Warranty. Will install or deliver for a fee. Flexible about designs, weights, and other items. Repairs as agreed in contract.

other work
Custom molds to be installed as form liners to pour concrete in place. Sculptured concrete: earth-cast, sand-cast, wood-formed, experimental.

This planter, an adaptation of a stylized Haida Indian chest, was a personal project that grew out of an interest in Northwest Indian art.

Spandrel, designed for a precast concrete office addition to a concrete warehouse, Vancouver Island. The commission came after a client saw the concrete planter above and wanted to have the same decorative Northwest Indian art in his office. The architect provided the blueprints, and Petty designed the panel, which was approved by both the client and the architect.

KEN WILLIAMS

505 West Tenth Street, Pueblo, CO 81003   (303) 542-1032

professional background
Williams has had many major commissions.

business practices
Quantity pricing available; otherwise, $40 to $50 per square foot; no minimum. Installation and shipping extra. Flexible about weight, color, and other specifications.

other work
Pottery, lamps, planters, and other items.

JOHN SUHAY

School District 60 Administration Building, Pueblo. The architect specified the area and the budget, and then Williams prepared a mock-up for the architect and owners. The project involved 5,000 brick units installed by brick masons.

JOHN SUHAY

Sangre de Cristo Arts and Conference Center, Pueblo (detail). The owners specified the area and the budget, and Williams was instructed to produce an original design. Brick masons did the installation.

DAVID BERFIELD

The Porcelain Company, 9461 Olson Road, Bainbridge Island, WA 98110 (206) 842-6210

professional background
Berfield has operated The Porcelain Company, a business that does graphic work on porcelain enamel, since 1978.

business practices
Jobs priced individually. Quantity pricing available; no minimum. Deposit sometimes required. No returns or cancellations. No warranty. Shipping included; installation not included. Color-matching available.

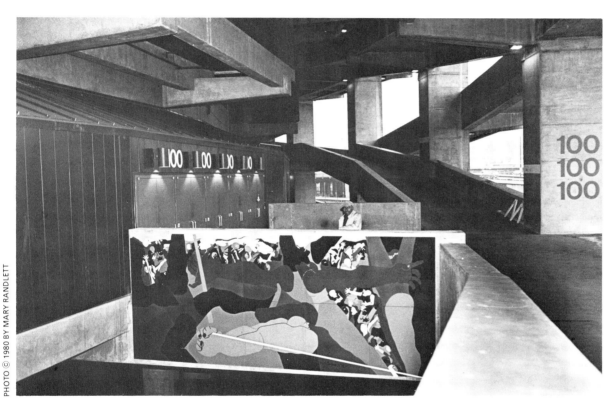

PHOTO © 1980 BY MARY RANDLETT

Games, *by Jacob Lawrence, 8 by 18 feet, porcelain enamel executed by David Berfield. Berfield provided technical advice on enlarging Lawrence's design and translating it to* porcelain enamel, color-matching the enamels and completing the mural — now in Seattle's Kingdome — under the artist's direction. Berfield can produce panels up to 42 by 60 inches.

PHOTO © 1980 BY MARY RANDLETT

Wall decoration, porcelain enamel, 8 by 21 inches. In this piece Berfield used the traditional porcelain enamel technique of spraying and brushing.

STEUART BREMNER

Metal River Foundry, Box 1287, Gunnison, CO 81230   (303) 641-2805 or 641-0539

professional background
With a partner Bremner has operated the Metal River Foundry in Gunnison since 1979. His work has been shown nationally.

business practices
Price range unlimited. Quantity pricing available; no minimum. Returns accepted. Credits given. Cancellations permitted. Deposit required for custom work. Warranty. Will install or ship for a fee.

other work
Gates, sculpture, and other hardware.

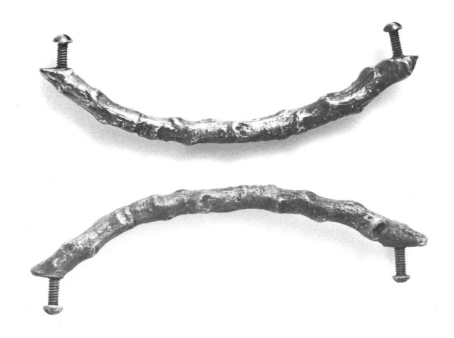

These drawer pulls are part of a group of hardware pieces used in cabinets in the home of a custom woodworker.

This faucet, photographed in a natural environment, has, because of its texture, a warmer appearance than the shiny objects usually found on a sink. Most of the work done in Bremner's foundry is custom-crafted. Bremner also does multiples.

LIN BROWER

Custom Iron Work, PO Box 93, Jerome, AZ 86331 (602) 634-8961

professional background

Brower has a long history of working with machinery, and for the past two years has been doing custom ironwork.

business practices

Quantity pricing available; otherwise, $8 to $30 per square foot; no minimum. Deposit required. Returns and cancellations accepted. Credits given. Warranty for normal use. Will install or ship for a fee.

other work

Chandeliers and anything unusual or unique.

Spanish-style gate with the suggestion of a phoenix in the arch. The design agreement with the clients was verbal, and they were so delighted with the result that they gave the craftsman a $100 tip.

Jerome Club House. The first design by Brower's associate Jaye Marchant for this gate installed in what formerly was the hospital of this historic mining town was eagerly accepted by all. The gate is frequently photographed by tourists who believe it is part of the original structure.

ALEXANDER BROWN

611 Baca Street, Santa Fe, NM 87501   (505) 983-9722 (studio) or 988-4393 (home)

professional background
Brown has worked with iron for 10 years.

business practices
Priced at $12 per hour plus materials. Quantity pricing on some items. No minimum. Deposit required. Returns and cancellations accepted. Credits given. Warranty. Will install or deliver for a fee.

other work
Railings, kitchen utensils, firescreens, and other items.

Stove in a restaurant in Tesuque, New Mexico. The clients knew Brown's work and left the design to him. They requested only that the stove heat a specific area and take up the least possible amount of floor space.

Gate, 5 feet by 40 inches. The client wanted to keep his dog out of the downstairs room. Brown submitted half a dozen drawings of different styles. Brown always submits drawings of various styles and can also work with blueprints.

TONY BUCHEN

515 Cortez, Santa Fe, NM 87501 (505) 988-4655

professional background
Buchen has a physics background. He recently took up blacksmithing full time.

business practices
Quantity pricing available; otherwise, $11 per hour; no minimum. No returns. Deposit required. Cancellations accepted. Warranty. Will install or ship for a fee. Works primarily by contract.

other work
Fireplace tools, kitchen utensils, window grills, and other items.

Another door in the house.

All the doors in this house have bar latch-type handles. Buchen was given a great deal of freedom in designing them. In this handle Buchen reflects the Indian designs in the house.

Detail of the shutter latch on the door. The contractor wanted a shutter latch with some sort of corn motif. He was pleased with the amount of detail.

SCOTT FREDENBURG

1010 11th Street, Boulder, CO 80310 (303) 499-1156 Gallery of Contemporary Metalsmithing, Deborah Norton, Director, 800 Powers Building, Rochester, NY (716) 546-1224

professional background
Fredenburg recently moved to Colorado from Illinois. He has exhibited widely, primarily in the Midwest.

business practices
No quantity pricing; no minimum. Deposit required. Returns accepted. No cancellations. Warranty. Will install or ship for a fee.

Gate, Southern Illinois University, Carbondale, Illinois. The gate was designed to be people-proof.

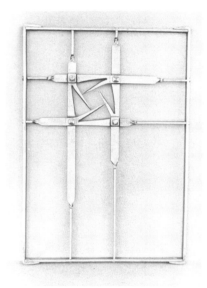

Window grille for a private house, 46 by 46 inches. Iron.

Iron wall sketch, Illinois State Museum. 32 by 22 inches. The sketch shows another design that could be used for a grille.

KEITH JELLUM

11535-C SW Tonquin Road, Sherwood, OR 97140   (503) 638-6344

professional background

Jellum has won various awards and had a number of exhibitions in the Northwest. Since 1973 he has lived on the sale of his work.

business practices

Priced at around $1,000 per linear foot; no quantity pricing. Deposit required. Warranty. No returns. Will install as contracted. Delivery time about a year. Jellum has had no problems with finished work.

other work

Cast-bronze sculpture and fountains.

This piece was produced on speculation and didn't find its home until later. Most of Jellum's work, however, is done on commission, where the owner or architect has a need for something in a certain spot. He is paid for the design, and when it is approved a contract is drawn up. All the pieces move easily with the wind.

The house itself was built in 1890. The cupola was a focal point that needed something, and the owner left it entirely up to Jellum to design one of his Windships for it. The shape of the cupola was considered in the design of the piece.

Jellum was not consulted until after the completion of this building. He then designed the vertical Windship to conform to the architecture.

JOHN KILLMASTER

220 Cotterell, Boise, ID 83709   (208) 385-1230 (work) or 375-8090 (home)

professional background
Killmaster is Professor of Art, Boise State University. He has an M.A. degree from Cranbrook and has had many commissions and fellowships.

business practices
Quantity pricing available; otherwise, $75 per square foot on murals; no minimum. Deposit required. Returns and cancellations accepted. Warranty. Installation and shipping included. Vitreous high-gloss enamel surface, large range of colors. Can be matte finish.

other work
Colored weather vanes, gargoyles, masks for wall reliefs, screens, lighting fixtures, tiles, architectural details, and other items.

Boise Gallery of Art, exterior wall. The gallery director and another artist judged the design and made suggestions. The final design was carefully rendered in airbrush. The model was closely followed in the finished work so the client would know what to expect. The work is on steel panels fired three times each to control the color consistency.

Close-up of wall.

DAVID PLATT & WILLIAM BRUDER

Architectural Sheetmetal Company, Box 4575, New River Stage One, 44020 North Circle Mount Road,
New River, AZ 85029 (602) 465-7720

professional background

Platt, a metal craftsman, and Bruder, a designer, work together to provide finely designed and crafted objects in metal to complement architecture.

business practices

Prices and terms depend on the project and the contract.

other work

Custom metal chairs, tables, telephone stands, roofs, shutters, doors, and any details involving metal design and craftsmanship.

Side of a house, showing exterior metal work. The inside of the curved walls is paneled in copper.

Sculptural duct work and pivoting doors. The carefully detailed duct work runs 74 feet along a skylight through this house. These copper-clad pivoting doors with flame patina are mounted on a sandblasted steel channel beam and serve as a room divider.

JOHN POWELL

Box 115, Bliss, ID 83314   (208) 352-4264

professional background

Powell has taught at Haystack School in Maine and Sun Valley Center in Idaho, and has studied in the Netherlands. He recently finished a large piece for the Boise Cascade Corporation.

business practices

Priced from $600 to $1200 per piece. No quantity pricing; no minimum. Deposit required. No returns. Warranty. Will install or ship for a fee.

other work

Wrought iron, monument sculpture, kitchen furniture.

Fireplaces. For these fireplaces, metalworker John Powell first submitted drawings which were approved by the client. Then a deposit was paid and work was begun.

MARK ROBERT SHEEHAN

PO Box 1815, Ketchum, ID 83340   (208) 726-3553

professional background
Sheehan has worked as a black-smith for over nine years.

business practices
Priced at $30 per hour plus materials. No quantity pricing; no minimum. Deposit required. No returns or cancellations. No warranty. Installation if in contract. Finishes may be painted, electro-plated, sandblasted, rusted, or done by other methods.

other work
Joist hangers, handrailings, candleholders, and anything a blacksmith would do.

Detail showing tulip.

Firescreen with tulips. This client had a series of etched glass windows with a tulip design. Sheehan suggested re-peating the design in the steel of the fireplace.

Firescreen. This fireplace of river rock was 30 feet high. Sheehan suggested a design to make the fireplace look less vertical and to provide a lower focal point for the room. Out of several designs submitted to the client, this one was chosen. Sheehan is accustomed to working in consultation with clients, interior designers, and architects.

PAOLO SOLERI

Cosanti Originals, 6433 Doubletree Road, Scottsdale, AZ 85253 (602) 948-6145

professional background
Soleri has received many grants and honorary degrees for his architectural and craftwork. His books include *Arcology: City in the Image of Man.*

business practices
Quantity pricing to outlets; otherwise, $200 to $15,000; no minimum. Deposit required. Returns and cancellations accepted. Credits. Warranty. Installation not included. Will ship by UPS. Six-week delivery time.

other work
Bronze sculpture and ceramic bells.

IVAN PINTAR

Soleri bells. In addition to being an architect, Soleri makes bells and metal sculptures. This piece was carved in styrofoam, then cast in bronze.

Soleri bells. Also made by the same styrofoam process.

TERRY TALTY

Metal River Foundry, PO Box 1287, Gunnison, CO 81230   (303) 641-2805

professional background
Talty is an owner of Metal River Foundry, Gunnison, Colorado.

business practices
Quantity pricing available; no minimum. Deposit required. Cancellations accepted. Credits given. Warranty. Will install or ship for a fee.

other work
Hardware, bathroom and kitchen accessories, and detailed metal castings.

Billiton Metals and Ores. *Talty's clients needed a particular metal object but had no idea of how it could be designed. The client chose this design from several presented.*

Creative Cook. *The entire apron is cast in bronze. All but the lettered area has a reddish-brown patina. This is a 12-inch model of a proposed sign for a store in Denver.*

BRUCE WEST

3018 SW Flower Terrace, Portland, OR 97201 (503) 245-0343

professional background
West is currently artist-in-residence at Lewis and Clark College, Portland. His work is in many collections, and he has received many public commissions.

business practices
Price depends on project. Each work is one of a kind. Installation and shipping included. Deposit required. No maintenance needed.

other work
Fireplaces.

Pittock Block Building lobby, Portland. This work in the foyer of a large office building is the focal point for people going in and out of the building. The client, architect, and artist all *agreed a large and powerful work was needed in this space above the elevators. The design, fabrication, and installation were done by West.*

Detail of clinic exterior.

Allergy Clinic exterior, Portland. In collaboration with architect John Storrs, West produced a design for a stainless-steel exterior wall. The design had to be visually appealing as well as functional. West also oversaw the fabrication and installation of the project.

WALTER A. WHITE
5126 Woodlawn Avenue North, Seattle, WA 98103   (206) 632-7391

professional background
White has an M.F.A. degree from the Rhode Island School of Design, and he exhibits nationally.

business practices
Priced from $350 to $1500; no quantity pricing; no minimum. Deposit required. No returns or cancellations. No warranty. Does not install. Will ship for a fee.

other work
Metal construction.

Scissors. *Seattle City Light commissioned this piece after seeing photographs of White's previous work. This percent-for-art project, forged from copper, is now outside the mayor's office in Seattle.*

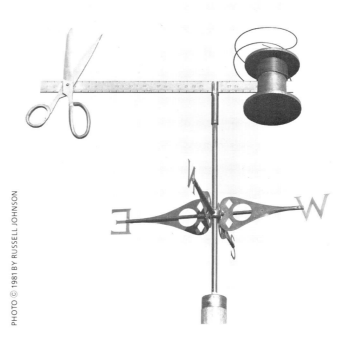

Detail of Scissors.

Fire truck. *White was hired to make a series of weather vanes for historic buildings while he was craftsman-in-residence for the city of Tacoma. The craftsman suggested this site on Engine House #11.*

GLORIA CROUSE

4325 John Luhr Road NE, Olympia, WA 98506   (206) 491-1980

professional background
Crouse has exhibited throughout the United States, Canada, and Japan since 1958.

business practices
Priced from $3,000 to $25,000. Only large-scale pieces. Deposit required. Warranty. Shipping and installation included. Flexible about color and other specifications.

other work
Fiber works. Many materials can be incorporated into the pieces.

Vocology III, *Sno-Isle Vocational Skills Center, Everett, Washington. Crouse's main concern here was to use the same theme (representative materials) without duplicating the work at Tacoma. Since this area had heavy traffic, durable materials had to be used.*

Vocology, *Clover Park Vocational Technical Institute, Tacoma. Crouse worked very closely with the Art Committee on this project for the Art in New Buildings Program. Objects were collected from the classrooms to illustrate the available courses offered. Everyone at the school —from administrators to students —became involved in the project.*

MURALS

KAY SLUSARENKO

1267 South Cherry Lane, Lake Oswego, OR 97034   (503) 636-6514 (home) or 636-8141 (work)

professional background
Slusarenko is chairman of the art department at Marylhurst College, Oregon, and has done many public murals.

business practices
Priced from $5,000 to $25,000. A written contract determines details and method of payment. Murals can be washed.

other work
Etched sandblast murals in concrete and brick walls, terrazzo and tile floors.

Cheney Junior High, Cheney, Washington. Slusarenko here worked with both the architect and the contractor in painting interior concrete walls and sandblasting panels for exterior walls. The theme was "Youth and Energy."

Oregon Automobile Insurance Company, Portland. The client requested that the murals for two floors not be dated and that the work tell the story of the Pacific Northwest Indians. The artist used symbols and color to show the animals, people, shelters, and landscape of the Northwest. Slusarenko always does a great deal of research to develop the theme for the project.

MARGARET AHRENS SAHLSTRAND

Icosa Studio and Paper Mill, Route 4, Box 279, Ellensburg, WA 98926   (509) 964-2341

professional background
Sahlstrand has exhibited her work nationally for a number of years.

business practices
Priced at $168.75 per square foot, including shipping and a Plexiglas box frame. Quantity pricing only for multiples of editioned work. No installation. Flexible about color and other specifications.

other work
Can treat entire walls, create translucent screens for windows and room dividers, make custom molds of garments, and other items.

Silverdale's Children, *Cottonwood Elementary School, Silverdale, Washington, handmade cast paper. Sahlstrand was chosen by a jury in the Art in New State Buildings Program, after which she made another presentation to the school committee, giving them the final choice of composition, colors, and fibers. They selected the motif of garments and plants. The interchange between the committee's "We would like . . ." and Sahlstrand's "I can do . . ." worked smoothly.*

Detail of another piece in the school building. The branch for the casting came from the schoolyard. Pieces are behind Plexiglas.

ROSANNA HALL

258½ B Staab, Santa Fe, NM 87501   (505) 988-5703
Canyon Road Gallery, Laurie Landis, Owner, 710 Canyon Road, Santa Fe, NM 87501   (505) 983-6831

professional background
Hall has been making screens over ten years and has agents as far away as Japan. She generally works with floral designs.

business practices
About $27 per square foot. Quantity pricing for similar or duplicate. No minimum. Deposit required. No returns. Cancellations accepted before approval. Will ship or install for a fee.

Flameproof. Flexible about color, size, and other specifications.

The oil painting design for this canvas screen in a summerhouse cocktail lounge was planned with the interior designers. The top part is blue with tropical flowers, and the bamboo at the bottom was taken from fabric used at a window in the room.

This iris fireplace screen was chosen by a client to cover the fireplace opening in the summertime. The screen could also be set on or hung over a sideboard. It is backed with a durable dark blue bookbinding fabric.

Closeup of the summerhouse screen.

SCOTT LAWRENCE

Scott Lawrence Company, 204 Third Avenue South, Seattle, WA 98104   (206) 621-9513 or 325-7518 (evenings)

professional background
Lawrence lived in Taiwan for two years while in an intensive Chinese language program. Since 1978 he has been the owner and designer-craftsman of Scott Lawrence Company.

business practices
Quantity pricing available; otherwise, $8.50 per square foot; no minimum; no returns; no credits or cancellations. Deposit required. Warranty. Will install for a fee, or a finish carpenter can install. Will ship for a fee. A catalog of Lawrence's work, and samples of the Fiberglas shoji "paper," are available upon request.

other work
Custom furniture and fine cabinetry.

PHOTO © 1980 BY MARY RANDLETT

This opening was fitted by the craftsman working from a measured sketch provided by the interior designer. As in most of his shoji installations, Lawrence here set up a classical tension between strong vertical and horizontal elements so that the elements neutralize each other.

SARA AND KENNETH HOPKINS

3319 SW Water Avenue, Portland, OR 97201   (503) 222-2903
Architectural Preservation Gallery, 26 NW Second Avenue, Portland, OR 97209   (503) 243-1923
FolkCraft Gallery, 302 SW First Avenue, Portland, OR 97204   (503) 222-5063

professional background
Sara and Kenneth Hopkins have been working together for about five years.

business practices
Restoration prices require estimates. Otherwise, the cost is $10 per square foot for the first two colors. Quantity pricing available; no minimum. Deposit required. Returns and cancellations ac-
cepted. Warranty. Installation not included, unless in contract. Flexible about colors and other specifications.

other work
Floor cloths and restoration.

Tumwater chairs, reproductions of an original rawhide seat chair with stenciled decoration produced in western Washington in the 1860s. The chair was made and decorated by hand for the State Capitol Museum in Olympia.

Stenciled floor cloth. Done with modern materials and methods, but with the purpose of following Victorian design.

Victoria's Nephew Restaurant in Portland. The building was stenciled and decorated by hand several times in the late 1880s and '90s. One complete original wall is intact. In this restoration project, the Hopkinses worked with the full cooperation of the restaurant staff and customers in an effort to preserve a rare example of late Victorian stencil decoration.

SALLY BACHMAN

1600 Valverde Street, PO Box 3327, Taos, NM 87571 (505) 758-1439
Clay and Fiber Gallery, PO Box 439, Taos, NM 87571 (505) 758-8093

professional background
Bachman has a degree in nursing. Since 1970, she has done weaving and teaching and given many shows. For three years she sold hand-dyed wool fibers.

business practices
About $130 per square foot; no quantity pricing; no minimum. No returns or cancellations. No warranty. Deposit required. Will ship for a fee.

other work
Pillows.

Spirit Trap. *Produced on speculation, 83 by 90 inches. The piece uses a somewhat contemporary Native American geometric pattern with several creative methods of dyeing wool to produce the illusion of three dimensions through the combined use of color and design.*

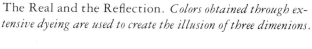

The Real and the Reflection. *Colors obtained through extensive dyeing are used to create the illusion of three dimenions.*

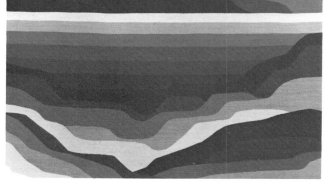

Reflections of the Spirits of the Waters. *This piece and most of Bachman's work reflect the influence of her surroundings and her contact with the Indians of the region. With her help clients choose from her styles and then discuss color.*

DANA BOUSSARD

Route 1, Arlee, MT 59821   (406) 726-3357

professional background
Boussard has many installations in major buildings in the Northwest, and she is now working on a commission for the Anchorage International Airport.

business practices
Approximately $100 per square foot; no quantity pricing; no minimum. No returns. Cancellations accepted. Deposit required. One-year warranty. Flameproof.

other work
Screens, complete wall coverings, acoustical dividers, and ceilings.

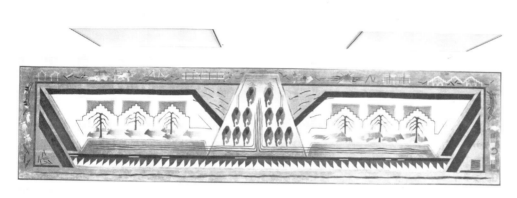

Overland Allegory, Wells Fargo Bank, Torrance, California. 4½ by 20 feet. Boussard is always concerned with how a piece fits both aesthetically and historically into an environment, and she is more than willing to cooperate with the architectural committee to achieve those ends.

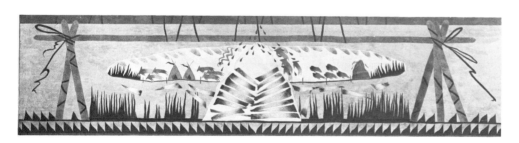

We Dreamed of the Way It Used To Be, 5 by 20 feet. This piece for a secondary school in Washington was commissioned through the percent-for-art program; it is based on the history of the area.

Through the Willamette, 4½ by 22¼ feet. Boussard was chosen from an open competition to do this piece at Portland State University.

DONNA CARYN BRAVERMAN

7920 East Camelback Road, #511, Scottsdale, AZ 85251   (602) 946-2633

professional background

Braverman has worked as an interior designer and photographer.

business practices

Quantity pricing available; otherwise, $600 per module; no minimum. No returns or cancellations. Deposit required. Warranty. Will install for a fee. Will ship by UPS or truck; add 8 percent for freight. Can flameproof. Eight weeks delivery for six modules.

PHOTO © 1980 BY DONNA BRAVERMAN

Study with 2-by-2-foot hand-dyed fiber modules. The six pieces stack together into a box 18 inches high. The overall design can easily be modified, since each piece hangs independently and can be hung at any angle. Installation is very easy. In all of her pieces Braverman wants to create a fiber art that adds warmth to and softens the lines of modern buildings. She works closely with clients, allowing them to select fiber type and color, and module shape. Sample shapes can be done with foam core scale models. The number of modules is flexible.

Detail of modules.

BARBARA HAND

304 South Second Street West, Missoula, MT 59801   (406) 549-3168

professional background

Hand has been a full-time professional weaver for the past four years. Her business is called By Hand.

business practices

Priced from $30 to $40 per square foot; no quantity pricing; no minimum. Returns accepted. No credits or cancellations. Warranty. Deposit required. Shipping included in price.

other work

Light, airy gauze-weave room dividers; window pieces.

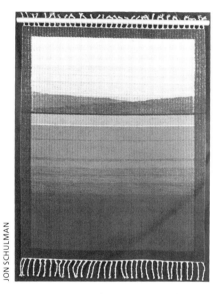

Wool rug, 50 by 65½ inches. This piece is one of a group of four. They are currently being shown in a bank in Missoula, where they are being considered for purchase. There this rug enhances a large open sitting area.

Blue and beige wool rug, 7 by 9 inches. The designs for this rug and another rug in the same room were arrived at in consultation with the client and the interior designer. The octagonal interior shape of this rug reflects the shape of the other one.

Wool area rug, 50 by 70 inches, in burgundy and red. The design was based on a fragment of Chinese architectural decoration. The rug is especially suited to a home with oriental furnishings.

ROBERT KASAL

3832 SW Corbett, Portland, OR 97201   (503) 228-6798

professional background
Kasal has worked as a designer for industry and theater. He currently works in textiles and teaches at Portland State University.

business practices
Price varies; quantity pricing available. No minimum. Deposit required. No returns. Cancellations accepted, but deposit not returned. Warranty as stated in contract. Shipping and installation included. Flameproof.

Flexible about weight and other specifications.

other work
Weavings and wall hangings.

Poolside installation. The client wanted a textile piece for the wall next to the pool. The piece would have to withstand moisture and go well with water.

Rope mural, Contemporary Crafts Gallery, Portland. The client, a non-profit organization, wanted something that was inexpensive but showed the warmth and subtlety possible in hand-made products so that passers-by would be inclined to come in.*

LARRY KIRKLAND

2122 NW Northrup, Portland, OR 97210   (503) 244-8595 (studio) or 223-4069 (home)

professional background
Kirkland has been self-employed as a fiber artist since 1976 and has major works from Texas to Alaska.

business practices
Kirkland does only fairly large pieces. Business details are worked out in each contract.

Serac, *University of Alaska, Anchorage. The piece was commissioned as the major campus artwork for a new complex of classroom and office buildings. It is composed of 2-foot-long acrylic rods and ³/₁₆-inch white nylon rope, and it hangs 27 feet down from the ceiling.*

Tsunami, *Arthur Andersen and Company, Portland. This focus for the reception area drops 30 feet from the ceiling.*

VERA WAINAR KOPECEK

514 East Oregon, Phoenix, AZ 85012   (602) 266-0355

professional background
Kopecek has studied in Czecho-slovakia and has been a weaver for many years.

business practices
Priced from $250 to $350 per square foot plus 10 percent design fee; no quantity pricing; minimum order required. Deposit required. No returns. Cancellations accepted, but no return of deposit. No warranty.

other work
Design for mosaics, stained glass, and hand-cut ceramic tiles for wall reliefs.

Memories. *This piece is based on memory fragments. Kopecek is accustomed to working with architects and can read architectural plans. She likes to consult with the architect and then prepare several solutions to the problem at hand. Visits to her studio while the work is in progress are welcome.*

My Stonehenge. *The composition with its vertical supports and horizontal beams represents Stonehenge. Kopecek tried to express the mystery of Stonehenge by tension between dark and light spaces, while also including the reds, pinks, and turquoise colors of Arizona and Indian art.*

CONSTANCE LaLENA

2851 Road B½, Grand Junction, CO 81503　(303) 242-3883

professional background
LaLena exhibits nationally and writes a regular column for *Inter-weave.* She is the author of *A Hand-book of Synthetic Dyes for the Fiber Arts,* published by Charles Scribner's Sons, New York.

business practices
Quantity pricing available; otherwise, $26 to $80 per running yard for standard fabrics; minimum order one yard. Catalog available. Custom fabrics also available. Deposit required. Returns accepted, credits given; no cancellations.

Warranty. No installation. Can arrange to have draperies made with fabrics. Will ship by UPS for small fee. Delivery time one to six weeks.

other work
Window coverings and floor coverings; architectural wall pieces.

 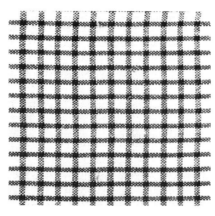 

Samples of 36 standard fabrics LaLena has available for upholstery and window treatments. She has developed over 1,000 dyes, and all her material is hand-dyed. She also does architectural wall pieces that she custom designs for each client.

STEFANIE DASH MARVEL

Box 90, Stanley, ID 83278 (208) 774-3593

professional background
Marvel has exhibited nationally.

business practices
No quantity pricing; no minimum. Deposit required. No returns. Will install free within 400 miles. Will ship free. Will flameproof if requested.

other work
Wall hangings and tapestries.

Another view of the same piece.

Linen weaving. This was a commissioned piece. After taking the architectural design, the proposed lighting, and the room's color scheme into account, Marvel proposed a design and discussed her color and ideas with the client. She will work with any client to achieve a successful and totally integrated fiberwork.

ANN MATLOCK

206 Camino Rio, Santa Fe, NM 87501 (505) 983-2488 (home) or 471-1495 (studio)
The Hand and the Spirit Gallery, 4222 North Marshall Way, Scottsdale, AZ 85251 (602) 946-4529

professional background
Matlock has taught weaving throughout the Southwest. She wrote reviews for *Craft Horizons.*

business practices
Priced from $60 to $75 per square foot; no quantity pricing; minimum of 3 by 5 feet. No returns, credits, or cancellations. Deposit required. Warranty. The work can be hung easily. Will ship for a fee.

other work
Watercolors, rugs, tunics, ponchos, and other items.

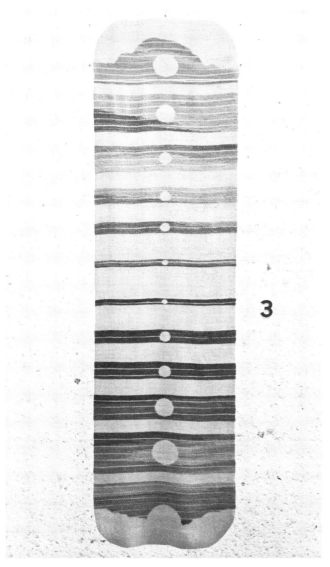

3

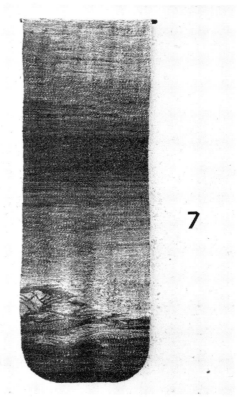

7

This piece too can be used either as a shawl or a wall hanging, as the client had specified. This client wanted darker colors than Matlock usually used. Matlock also takes architectural commissions.

Moon. *Handspun, natural-dyed tussah silk, 2 by 7 feet. The piece follows a full moon from its rising to its setting. It can either be hung on the wall or used as a shawl.*

PAM PATRIE

4314 NE 22nd, Portland, OR 97211   (503) 224-9916

professional background

Patrie has exhibited nationally and has had many public commissions.

business practices

Approximately $100 per square foot; less for quantity; no minimum. Deposit required. Returns accepted, credits given. No cancellations. Warranty. Will ship by UPS for a fee.

other work

Works used for acoustical systems to help solve problems with sound.

Kaiser Permanente Medical Clinics. Patrie was commissioned to design and produce tapestries that could be rotated in a collection of works throughout two medical clinics. She worked closely with the project director and chose themes that would be pleasing to patients. She is accustomed to working closely with clients.

Civic Auditorium, Portland. This piece in blues and greens was selected by the city of Portland to brighten a lounge area of the Civic Auditorium. The piece was to be viewed from a distance of 20 to 30 feet.

LYNNE REEVE

1619 Cornell NE, Albuquerque, NM 87106   (505) 255-9656

professional background
Born in England, Reeve has a master's degree from the Royal College of Art. She also has an extensive background in pottery.

business practices
Blind in the first photograph, $80. No reduction for large orders; no minimum. No returns or cancellations. Deposit required. Warranty through installation. Very flexible about color, material, and other specifications. Will ship by UPS for a fee.

other work
Glazes and clay bodies, functional domestic pottery, and commercial ware.

Heavy cotton twill blind. Reeve uses a simple system of screw-eyes, wooden dowels, and a double hook for winding the cord on the wall that produces a failsafe blind that works efficiently at any size. The fabric is easily removed for machine washing. The blinds are reversible, and the same design can be used as a room divider.

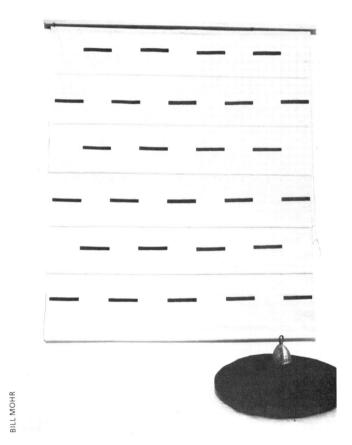

This blind for a large, low window needed a design to go with the almost temple-like simplicity and tranquility of the room. Reeve bases her designs on the ideas the clients give her for the atmosphere they want in a particular room. She then gives them several sketched solutions, and is always willing to comply with their suggestions.

BILL MOHR

BILL MOHR

ROWEN SCHUSSHEIM

2335 West Carson Drive, Tempe, AZ 85282   (602) 968-3813

professional background
Schussheim is on the faculty at
Arizona State University in the
Fiber Arts Department.

business practices
Priced at about $60 per square
foot; no quantity pricing; no minimum. Deposit required. Returns
accepted. No cancellations. Warranty. Will install or ship for a
fee. Will flameproof if requested.

Flexible about color and other
specifications.

other work
Wall hangings.

Sideswiped. *This environmental piece has seven forms hanging by monofilament from the ceiling. It is installed over a
large stairwell in the Scottsdale Center for the Arts, Arizona,
and is part of the permanent collection. In this case the piece
was purchased after its completion, although Schussheim is
quite willing to work with clients and their particular needs
in the design of a piece. She generally provides sketches and
sometimes a small model of the large work.*

CAROL SHINN

2105 West De Palma, Mesa, AZ 85202 (602) 833-4538

professional background
Shinn has exhibited widely in the South and Southwest.

business practices
Wholesale price $32 to $40 per square foot; no quantity pricing; no minimum. No returns or cancellations. Deposit required. Warranty. Does not install but will ship by UPS at their rates.

other work
Three-dimensional pieces for walls or to hang freely; upholstery fabric.

Three panels done for American Express, who wanted the panels to go with new furniture and to use the color of the American Express trademark. Shinn used motifs from the upholstery fabric and arranged the elements into a landscape that included a nearby landmark. Designs were presented on two occasions, the second design being a refinement of the first with the help of the client and the interior designer. Shinn feels it is essential to be flexible in working with prospective clients.

This piece in a performance center in Scottsdale has additional texture on the surface to add softness to the architectural setting.

SUSAN SINGLETON

5565 NE Ambleside Road, Seattle, WA 98105   (206) 525-0975
Winn Gallery, Design Center Northwest #200, 5701 6th Avenue South, Seattle, WA 98108

professional background
Singleton has taught fibers at several schools and currently is interested in doing more soft sculpture pieces.

business practices
Price depends on project. No quantity pricing. No minimum. Deposit required. Returns and cancellations accepted. Warranty. Will install and ship for a fee. Can flameproof. Flexible about color and other specifications.

other work
Wall hangings, banners, large-scale kites, room dividers, and other items.

Sculptural piece designed for the Architecture Building at the University of Washington, Seattle. This large piece (35 feet long) of nylon and aluminum was a gift to the school from an alumni group. Several architects commissioned Singleton to do the piece. She is pleased with how its marriage of sculpture and fabric humanizes, softens, and warms the environment. She is accustomed to working with designers and architects.

JANET TAYLOR

1012 East Palmcroft Drive, Tempe, AZ 85282   (602) 967-3692
The Hand and the Spirit Gallery, 4222 North Marshall Way, Scottsdale, AZ 85251   (602) 946-4529

professional background

Taylor has been Assistant Professor of Art at Arizona State University since 1976. She has worked as a designer, has exhibited widely, and has given many workshops and lectures.

business practices

Priced from $90 to $125 per square foot; no quantity pricing; no minimum. A design fee is due after presentation of painted studies. Then a contract is made calling for three payments. Will install or ship for a fee.

Detail of a piece in an office in Phoenix. The 20th-floor office had a view of the desert and mountains. Taylor and the interior designer agreed to have the tapestries relate to the view. A total of six tapestries will be done.

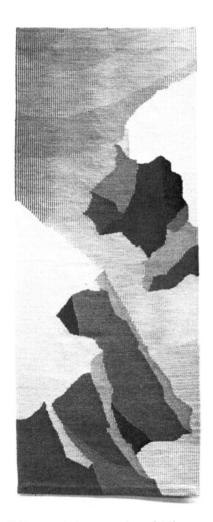

This commission came through The Hand and the Spirit Gallery in Scottsdale, Arizona. Taylor met with the clients in their home, showed slides and painted studies, and after discussion the work proceeded. The piece is 21 by 57 inches.

CHARLENE VOGEL

PO Box 14, Manzanita, OR 97130   (503) 368-6234   Wayne Martin, Inc., 210 NW 21st, Portland, OR 97209
(503) 221-2555   Jane Piper Reid & Co., 1000 Lenora, Seattle, WA 98121   (206) 621-9290

professional background

Vogel produces and markets her designed fabrics under the trade name of C. Vogel Fabrics. She markets in showrooms in Portland and Seattle.

business practices

Priced from $30 to $75 per yard; usually no quantity pricing; minimum order of two to five yards. Returns accepted. Credits given. No cancellations. Deposit required. Color is first approved from a sample. Fabric is sold by the yard; designer will install. Shipping extra. Delivery in two to six weeks.

other work

Yardage for various purposes: hangings, upholstery, and others.

Draperies and matching pillows for a condominium in Cannon Beach, Oregon. Vogel matched the color of the bedspreads provided by the interior designer. The wave pattern is part of her collection and was chosen to go with the overall beach atmosphere.

Roman shade in the kitchen of the same condominium. Vogel also did a wall hanging and pillows for the living room. The interior designer chose colors and patterns from Vogel's samples.

TOM ANDERSON

Creative Openings, 1013 West Holly Street, Bellingham, WA 98225   (206) 671-7435

professional background
Anderson has been working with wood since he was a child. He works mainly on doors.

business practices
Basic price varies with amount of lumber. Quantity pricing available; no minimum. No cancellations. Has had no returns. Deposit required. Satisfaction guaranteed. Installation not included. Will ship.

other work
Bronze door knockers and custom carving on doors.

Both screen doors are on a house in California. The client decided on the designs after examining Anderson's custom catalog along with some original and specialty items.

FEDERICO ARMIJO
400 Rio Grande NW, Albuquerque, NM 87104   (505) 243-5887 (showroom) or 831-6900 (studio)

professional background
Currently working in wood, metal, and stone, Armijo has studied many techniques in the Philippines, Hawaii, and Japan. He exhibits nationally.

business practices
Commission work: price in contract. Multiples in contract give quantity pricing; no minimum. Deposit required. No cancellations. Warranty. Installation and shipping as in contract. Large variety of work.

other work
Door handles, furniture, sculpture, and anything in wood, metal, or stone.

DICK KENT

DICK KENT

Armijo makes both wooden doors and their metal handles. His primary interest is doors, but when he was unable to find handles that appealed to him, he began to produce metal handles to conform to his door style. He is very happy to do custom work in which he incorporates ideas from the client into his designs. The two doors of which details are shown were produced on speculation.

KIRK BONDS

3134B Rufina, Santa Fe, NM 87501   (505) 983-2488

professional background
Since 1975, Bonds has been a self-employed finish carpenter and a cabinet and furniture maker.

business practices
No quantity pricing; no minimum. No returns or cancellations. Bonds works under a contract for design, allowing ample time for consultation with the customer. Deposit required. Warranty. Shipping extra.

other work
Furniture and architectural built-ins.

Hand-carved cherry table set. The design comes from art nouveau, although modern lamination processes are necessary for the construction. The method of joining the legs to the top is, to the best of Bonds's knowledge, his own. Much of his work stems from art nouveau and art deco.

Double rocker, made of maple. The design is an interpretation of the seldom-seen double rocker Bonds saw while growing up in central Texas. The shape of the seat and back is taken from a design available from the American Furniture Maker's Association.

Detail showing connection of leg and top.

ARNOLD CHERULLO & HELEN MELNIS

ARC Handcrafted Wood Constructions, 5310 Ballard Avenue NW, Seattle, WA 98107   (206) 784-4243

professional background
Since 1975, Cherullo and Melnis have run their ARC Handcrafted Wood Constructions.

business practices
Quantity pricing available; no minimum. Fifty percent deposit. Returns accepted. No cancellations. Warranty. Will install or ship for a fee.

other work
Toys, sculpture, furniture, and cabinets, both traditional and contemporary.

Primary shop identification sign, overhead. Hand-painted lettering. The tree in the center is a weathervane.

Sidewalk sign designed to complement and reaffirm the message of the overhead sign.

Flanking information signs. Signs rotate. One has "Open" backed by "Closed." The other has shop hours backed by a clock that tells what time the shop will reopen. In all work, the client's ideas are encouraged, and the craftsmen are guided by the client's specifications, requirements, and budgets.

DOUGLAS AND JONELLE COURTNEY

120 NW 23rd, Portland, OR 97210   (503) 248-9984

professional background
Since 1976, Douglas and Jonelle have operated their Pro-forma Designs, Inc., featuring a variety of woodwork.

business practices
Design fee. Quantity pricing available; otherwise, $35 per man-hour plus materials and installation; no minimum. Deposit required. No returns or cancellations. Warranty. Will ship and install for a fee. Variety of finishes.

As flexible about specifications as possible.

other work
Curved railings, office furniture, executive desks, and other items.

French fireplace facade. The Courtneys were given the general design by the client and the designer. Walnut was chosen to go with the dark marble. Despite its size the facade had to remain light and delicate.

Fireplace facade (detail). In the same room on the opposite wall was an oak-paneled dining room wall salvaged from an old Portland hotel. The Courtneys completely redid the rest of the room, including the fireplace, to match the salvaged wall.

Fireplace facade with wood box. For this piece the designer had detailed plans. The client approved construction drawings, and work began.

BOB EASTON

Box 2785, Santa Fe, NM 87501 (505) 983-2272

professional background
Easton has been working in wood since 1974. His work appears in a variety of buildings.

business practices
Will bid on specific pieces. Deposit. No returns or cancellations. Warranty. Can install or ship for a fee.

other work
Spinning wheels: the Rio Grande Wheel.

This door is in a house that is an historic landmark built in the traditional Santa Fe adobe style. This design was selected by the client from preliminary drawings.

This door on a mosque in Abiquiu, New Mexico, has for its design an Arabic phrase written in a traditional calligraphic style. The design was given to Easton to execute as he saw fit.

These doors in the same mosque were adapted from a traditional design in a book on Arab architecture written by the architect with whom Easton was working on this project.

JOHN ECONOMAKI

2834 NE 39th, Portland, OR 97212 (503) 282-6995

professional background
A woodworker for some time, Economaki constantly tries to simplify forms.

business practices
No quantity pricing; no minimum. Deposit required. Returns and cancellations accepted. Warranty. Will install or deliver for a fee.

other work
Doors, desks, tables, conference tables, chairs, and other items.

PHOTO © 1981 BY JOSEPH FELZMAN

Gallery bench. This piece was designed to allow people to sit while viewing large paintings.

PHOTO © 1981 BY JOSEPH FELZMAN

Serving trolley for a Portland restaurant. The owner of the restaurant specified the height and these additional requirements: that it have a silverware drawer and a shelf for French pastries, that it be easily maneuverable in close quarters, and that it be expandable and attractive. Economaki came up with this design and since then has had orders for several more.

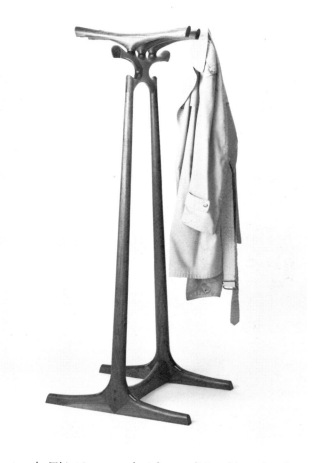

PHOTO © 1981 BY JOSEPH FELZMAN

Coat rack. This piece started with a traditional base, but for the top Economaki played with the pun relating a coat rack and a rack of horns, and coats are hung on a stylized antler.

CURTIS ERPELDING

110 Union Street, #300, Seattle, WA 98101   (206) 625-0754

professional background
Erpelding has had numerous shows and awards, including a $10,000 NEA grant to study knockdown design.

business practices
Priced at $20 per hour for labor. Deposit required. Warranty. No returns, credits, or cancellations. Installation and shipping available. Delivery in 6 to 12 months.

other work
Chairs, bed frames, armoires, and other items.

"Orientable." Currently used by its owners as a dining table, this piece knocks down completely: there is no metal hardware, only wedges attaching the legs, stretchers, and top. The drawer holds silverware and napkins.

Knockdown writing table. The table, in keeping with Erpelding's style, knocks down, the connecting joints being secured with wedges. The left half of the top can be raised in increments to 45 degrees. The right half lifts to reveal a storage compartment.

Stacking bookcases. The bookcases, here shown with three units, can be expanded both vertically and laterally, and could incorporate shelf units of different heights, which could also be used as display cases. Here, as in all of Erpelding's work, a client could specify dimensions and make suggestions about design.

GEOFFREY FITZWILLIAM

478 First Avenue, Salt Lake City, UT 84103   (801) 363-4985

professional background
Fitzwilliam has made violins. He was born in Flin Flon, Manitoba.

business practices
Quantity pricing available; no minimum. Deposit required. No returns. Cancellations accepted. Warranty. Installation and shipping included. Delivery time negotiable.

other work
Cabinetry, built-in furniture, signs, carpentry.

Psaltery table. Reproduced from a photograph of a 15th-century Chinese piece provided by a client. Every element in the piece is influenced by the design of every other element.

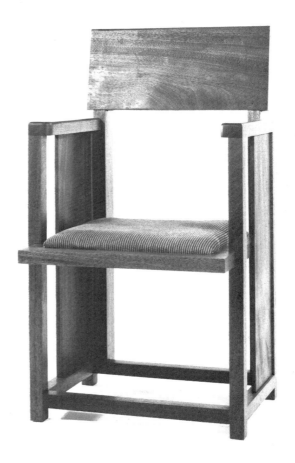

Dining chair from a Frank Lloyd Wright design of 1925. It was built on speculation to show that straight lines can have elegance and sophistication, often less expensively than other designs.

Lacquered coffee table. The client here wanted a Chinese piece in black lacquer. The styling is 15th-century Chinese, but the dimensions and proportions are Fitzwilliam's own. He believes a craftsman should be able to do the research and modification necessary for this type of work.

KATE JOYCE

4130 Blakely Avenue, Bainbridge Island, WA 98110   (206) 842-6481

professional background
Joyce has run the Kate Joyce Company, Design Woodwork, since 1974. She was apprenticed in 1972 and 1973 in Brienz, Switzerland.

business practices
Quantity pricing available; otherwise, approximately $200 to $350 per linear foot; no minimum. No returns. Cancellations permitted. Deposit required. Warranty. Installation and shipment for fee. Three to six months' delivery.

other work
All forms of woodwork.

SCOTT TAYLOR

DWIGHT FREEMAN

Entertainment furnishings, koa and birch. In the foreground is the bar with a liquor cabinet. The client wanted louvered doors. The dowel-louvers (patent pending) allow circulation but are easier to dust and oil than traditional louvers. Bar stools are in the background. In the far background are wall units.

Side chair, Nicaraguan walnut with leather. One of six chairs commissioned from a prototype, built on speculation, for formal chairs required for business meetings. The platform at the base provides stability and storage. The chair may be inverted for use as a side table.

STEVE SOLTAR

Dining table, curly Western maple. The client wanted an oriental or exotic table to seat six, but was able to extend it to seat ten. Two side tables (not shown) were designed to allow extension to 8 feet and to provide sideboards when not used with the main table.

TIM MACKANESS

3125 SE Van Waters, Portland, OR 97222   (503) 653-5230

professional background
Mackaness has done many major installations in the Northwest and has had his work shown in many exhibitions and publications.

business practices
Minimum order of $8,000. Deposit required. Cancellations permitted. Warranty. No credits and no returns. Installation and shipping included.

other work
Custom woodwork.

JACK W. SANDERS

Detail of handrailing, Oregon School of Arts and Crafts. Mackaness worked with a building committee and the architect to design the railing. For the execution he worked with lathe expert Walter Huber.

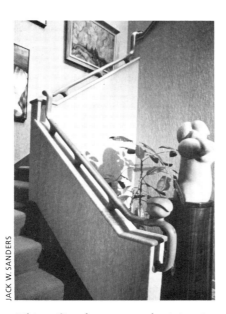

JACK W. SANDERS

This railing for a new condominium in Portland was designed after the client had seen the one at the Oregon School of Arts and Crafts.

JACK W. SANDERS

Detail of the condominium railing.

JOHN MASON

537 Sixth Avenue, Salt Lake City, UT 84103 (801) 355-1313
Sipapu Studio, 916 West South Temple Street, Salt Lake City, UT 84104 (801) 531-0232

professional background
Mason has worked in construction for many years. Now, with a partner, he runs Sipapu Studio, which has two employees.

business practices
Builds to order. No minimum. Deposit required. No returns or cancellations. Warranty. Installation included. Will ship for a fee.

other work
Mantles, doors, grills and screens, windows, desks, jewelry boxes, and other items.

Breakfast area, remodeled. Mason replaced pine cabinets with red oak ones, lowered the counter, and salvaged the windows.

In a new house in which Mason built all the casework and cabinets and some of the furniture, this is a large (16-by-16-foot) kitchen with a center island.

The cabinets in this kitchen were built in large sections and installed with open shelves and other labor-saving devices.

MARK NEWMAN

11220 Tonquin Road, Sherwood, OR 97140   (503) 638-4762

professional background

Newman works in his own shop on five acres near Sherwood. He has worked with interior designers and was featured in the 1980 "Street of Dreams" in Lake Oswego, Oregon.

business practices

No quantity pricing; no minimum. Deposit required. Returns and cancellations accepted. Credits given. Warranty. Will install and ship for a fee. Delivery time two to six months.

other work

Weaving looms, cabinets, rails, architectural detailing, and desks.

Solid cherry telephone desk.

Hutch, Oregon black walnut. Newman designed and built the piece for a client who wanted a place to display art objects as well as an enclosed storage space. The entire piece came from one log, and the grain patterns help unify it.

BALI OAKES

Box 205, Lincoln City, OR 97367

professional background
Oakes has a design background. He has been a self-employed designer-craftsman for the past three years.

business practices
Priced at $500 per week plus expenses. No quantity pricing. No minimum. Deposit required. Returns and cancellations accepted. Warranty. Installation and shipping included. Oiled or varnished surfaces.

other work
Wooden playground furnishings, railings, furniture, sculpture, and glasswork.

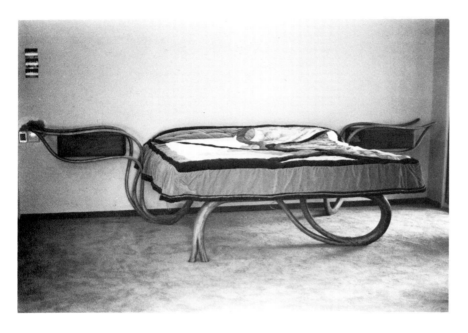

Bed. The client wanted a custom bed that would integrate with his room. There would be one chair in the room, and the bed was to have side tables. The rest of the space was open, with sliding doors leading to a patio. Oakes designed the bed to be light and airy, conforming with the atmosphere of the room. The color of the wood was decided after consultation with the interior designer.

Frame of the bed.

JOEL SHEPARD

12419 NE 124th, Kirkland, WA 98033   (206) 823-4545

professional background

Since 1976, Shepard has operated his own studio, designing and producing custom-made furniture and antique reproductions, and making repairs. He has had many commissions, including one in 1981 from an Arabian prince.

business practices

Materials plus $25 per hour; quantity pricing on items like chairs; no minimum. Deposit required. No returns. Cancellations accepted. Warranty. Installs and ships for a fee. Variety of finishes.

other work

Kitchens, entry doors, etched glass panels, and all forms of house furniture except upholstered.

Dining table with 12 chairs. Again he worked with the interior designers and the client. This is a walnut table with hand-laid-up walnut veneers and maple chairs.

Walnut cabinets. The craftsman worked with interior designers and the client, considering materials, detailing, and design alternatives. The final design went well with the very fine European antiques the house already had.

Detail of table.

JOHN SHERIFF

184 Osage Place SW, Albuquerque, NM 87105   (505) 831-0714

professional background

Sheriff has had various shows in New Mexico and has had his work published in *Fine Woodworking*.

business practices

No quantity pricing; no minimum. No credits or cancellations. Returns accepted. Deposit required. Warranty. Will ship. Delivery time: two to six months.

DAVID McMULLEN

Chest of drawers, brown ash cabinet, teak stand and pulls. The floating motif of the top is a common feature of Sheriff's work. The piece was produced on speculation as an entertaining exercise in detail and patience. Although most of his work is speculative and he wants freedom even on commissioned work, he is happy to make the pieces fit the desired function.

ROBERT RECK

Cabinet, goncalo alves (a South American hardwood) and ebony. The front of the cabinet is subtly curved by a process called coopering, and then smoothed with hand planes Sheriff made especially to fit the curve of the doors.

DAVID SIMON & WILLIAM TONEY

306 SE 30th Place, Portland, OR 97214 (503) 236-1721

professional background
Simon and Toney have been part-ners since 1974, and show together and individually.

business practices
Quantity pricing for duplicate work; otherwise, $18 per man-hour; no minimum. Deposit re-quired. No returns. Cancellations accepted. Warranty. Installation included, if in contract. Finishes can be oiled, varnished, or waxed.

Will be as flexible as possible to suit client.

other work
Woodwork of all kinds.

Pulpit. This is one of four pieces de-signed and built for this church. Simon and Toney submitted drawings and wood and joinery samples for approval by the architect and the church design committee.

Desk, book stand, and cabinet. These pieces were all experimental, to solve design problems.

MICHAEL STRONG

1133 14th Street, Bellingham, WA 98225 (206) 671-9952
Signature Gallery, 551 Pacific Avenue, San Francisco, CA 94133 (415) 986-5515

professional background

Strong has studied in Sweden. He recently had a one-man show at the College of Architecture, University of Washington, Seattle.

business practices

Chairs cost $300 to $900 retail. Quantity pricing on some items. No minimum. No cancellations or returns. Deposit required. Will ship for a fee.

DAVID SCHERRER

This chair with an adjustable back resulted from a long fascination with many parts working together toward one purpose. This piece was commissioned, and Strong consciously related the verticals and horizontals of the piece to similar lines in the room in which it would be installed.

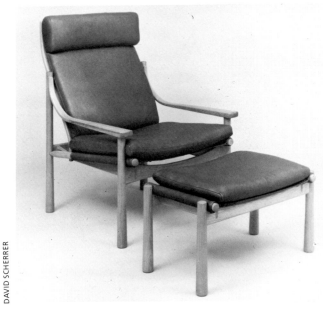

DAVID SCHERRER

This set is a companion to the chair. It has a deerskin cover.

DAVID SCHERRER

In this set the pivotal piece for Strong is the chair. The table's legs are similar to the chair's and make the pieces recognizable as a set.

RANDY TURNER

32621 SE Third Street, Carnation, WA 98014   (206) 788-2021 or 333-4589

professional background

Turner has sold his work throughout the West and has had various one-man shows in Washington. He has a series of room-divider screens in a hotel in Chicago.

business practices

Priced from $80 to $1000; quantity orders over $1,000 less 10 percent; no minimum. Deposit required. No returns or cancellations. Warranty. Will ship for a fee. Finished with hand-rubbed linseed oil. Color and finish can be changed.

Turner's pieces are made from willow shoots gathered from creek and river valleys in Washington. The shoots are bent and nailed in place when green, then left to dry and harden for three months. If they are used outside, they need oiling every six months to keep the bark from peeling. The color will vary from light orange to dark red depending on the exposure to sunlight. Turner can adapt to specific needs of clients.

PAUL VON ROSENSTIEL

603 Lake Washington Boulevard East, Seattle, WA 98112 (206) 328-1725

professional background
Von Rosenstiel has been a self-employed designer and builder since 1973.

business practices
No quantity pricing. No minimum. Deposit required. No returns. Cancellations accepted. Warranty. Will install (price depends on location). Will ship for a fee.

other work
Lighting and architecture.

Door knocker and security peephole. Von Rosenstiel incorporated both functions into one object. When the wood plug is removed from the door knocker, it is possible to see who is at the door.

Knocker on the outside.

Security peephole from the inside.

Detail of roller mechanism.

Sliding door and china cupboard. Von Rosenstiel designed and built the entire house. The client did not want to be cut off from guests while she was working in the kitchen, but she also didn't want the kitchen mess to be exposed to the guests' view. The sliding door and china cabinet (which do not go to the ceiling) allow the openness she wanted, but the door can be closed to hide the food-preparation disorder. The china cupboard opens on both sides.

STEVE VOORHEIS

401½ West Railroad Street, Missoula, MT 59802   (406) 728-5911

professional background
In 1979, with a partner, Voorheis established the Primrose Center, a private academy for teaching furniture design and construction. He is currently the director.

business practices
Priced from $1,000 to $10,000. No quantity pricing; no minimum. No returns or cancellations. Deposit required. Warranty. Will ship for a fee. Delivery time two to six months.

other work
Furniture of his design to fit customers' needs.

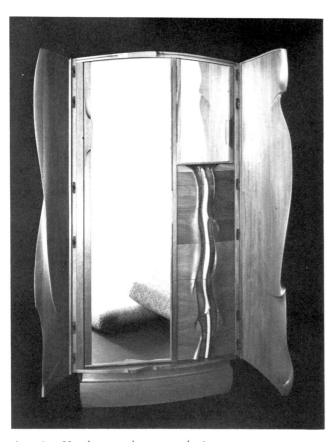

Armoire, Honduras mahogany and mirrors.

Linen cabinet of Honduras mahogany, wall mounted. Voorheis sees the elemental structure in his work as the box. His pieces are sophisticated variations.

List of Craftsmen

Candyce Anderson: *Lighting*, Washington, 73
Tom Anderson: *Wood*, Washington, 127
Federico Armijo: *Metals, Wood*, New Mexico, 38, 128
Sally Bachman: *Textiles*, New Mexico, 110
Harold Balazs: *Metals, Concrete*, Washington, 6, 35*
Philipp Baldwin: *Metal*, Oregon, 11, 16*
Robert Karl Behrens: *Wood*, Colorado, 83
David Berfield: *Metals*, Washington, 89
Deanna Lee Birkholm: *Glass*, Montana, 62
Kirk Bonds: *Wood*, New Mexico, 129
Dana Boussard: *Textiles*, Montana, 37, 111
Frank Boyden: *Lighting, Metals, Ceramics*, Oregon, 13, 74
Donna Caryn Braverman: *Textiles*, Arizona, 112
Stewart Bremner: *Metals*, Colorado, 90
Lin Brower: *Metals*, Arizona, 91
Alexander Brown: *Metals*, New Mexico, 92
William Bruder: *Metals*, Arizona, 8, 97
Tony Buchen: *Metals*, New Mexico, 93
Glenn Burris: *Lighting*, Oregon, 75
Ed Carpenter: *Glass*, Oregon, 7, 31, 63
Arnold Cherullo: *Wood*, Washington, 130
Chanson Ching: *Ceramics*, Montana, 40
Carl Christensen: *Ceramics*, New Mexico, 41
Douglas and Jonelle Courtney: *Wood*, Oregon, 131
Gloria Crouse: *Miscellaneous (Murals)*, Washington, 104
Bob Easton: *Wood*, New Mexico, 132
John Economaki: *Wood*, Oregon, 133
Garth Edwards: *Glass*, Oregon, 64
Kenneth Emerson: *Lighting*, Nevada, 76
Curtis Erpelding: *Wood*, Washington, 134
David Fernandez: *Lighting, Ceramics*, Utah, 42, 77
Geoffrey Fitzwilliam: *Wood*, Utah, 135
Jim Foster: *Ceramics*, Colorado, 43
Scott Fredenburg: *Metals*, Colorado, 94
Carl Freedman: *Metals*, Oregon, 8*
William T. Gilbert: *Ceramics*, New Mexico, 44
Tim Girvin: *Metals*, Washington 14, 18*
Mark Eric Gulsrud: *Glass*, Washington, 65
Barbara Grygutis: *Ceramics*, Arizona, 33, 45
Rosanna Hall: *Miscellaneous (Painted Screens)*, New Mexico, 107
Vicki Halper: *Ceramics*, Oregon, 46
Marge Hammond-Farness: *Masonry & Concrete*, Oregon, 14, 18, 84
Barbara Hand: *Textiles*, Montana, 32, 113
Douglas Hansen: *Glass*, Washington, 66
Frederick Heidel: *Glass*, Oregon, 34, 67
Lu Himes: *Wood*, Oregon, 7*
Sara and Kenneth Hopkins: *Miscellaneous (Stenciled Decoration/Restoration)*, Oregon, 109
Nancy Jacquot: *Ceramics*, Wyoming, 47
Keith Jellum: *Metals*, Oregon, 18, 36, 95
Barbara Jensen-Lamont: *Ceramics*, Oregon, 49
Kate Joyce: *Wood*, Washington, 136
Robert Kasal: *Textiles*, Oregon, 114
Michael Kennedy: *Glass*, Washington, 68
John Killmaster: *Metals*, Idaho, 96
Larry Kirkland: *Textiles*, Oregon, 21, 115
Allan Kluber: *Ceramics, Lighting*, Oregon, 35, 48, 78
Vera Wainar Kopecek: *Textiles*, Arizona, 116
Constance LaLena: *Textiles*, Colorado, 117

Mick Lamont: *Ceramics*, Oregon, 49
Scott Lawrence: *Miscellaneous (Paper Screen)*, Washington, 108
Don Lelooska: *Wood*, Washington, 6*
Joan Lincoln: *Ceramics*, Arizona, 50
Tim Mackaness: *Wood*, Oregon, 137
Paul Marioni: *Glass*, Washington, 69
N. Skreko Martin: *Ceramics*, Arizona, 51
Stefanie Dash Marvel: *Textiles*, Idaho, 118
John Mason: *Wood*, Utah, 138
Molly Mason: *Masonry & Concrete*, New Mexico, 85
Ann Matlock: *Textiles*, New Mexico, 119
Howard Meehan: *Glass*, Oregon, 29, 33, 70
Helen Melnis: *Wood*, Washington, 130
Juan and Patricia Navarrete: *Masonry & Concrete*, New Mexico, 34, 86
Joyce Newman: *Ceramics*, Colorado, 17, 52
Mark Newman: *Wood*, Oregon, 139
Bali Oakes: *Wood*, Oregon, 140
Tim O'Neil: *Glass*, Oregon, 29*
Jeanne Otis: *Ceramics*, Arizona, 53
Ralph Pardington: *Ceramics*, New Mexico, 54
Pam Patrie: *Textiles*, Oregon, 120
Ronald Petty: *Masonry & Concrete*, Washington, 87
David Platt: *Metals*, Arizona, 8, 97
Richard Posner: *Glass*, Washington, 71
John Powell: *Metals*, Idaho, 98
Mark Pratt: *Lighting*, Oregon, 79
Lynne Reeve: *Textiles*, New Mexico, 121
William Richards: *Ceramics*, Washington, 55
Sandra Robishaw: *Ceramics*, Colorado, 36, 56
John Rogers: *Lighting, Ceramics*, Oregon, 20, 80
Margaret Ahrens Sahlstrand: *Miscellaneous (Paper)*, Washington, 106
Carolyn Sale: *Ceramics*, New Mexico, 57
Georgia Sartoris: *Ceramics*, Colorado, 35, 58
Rowen Schussheim: *Textiles*, Arizona, 122
Mark Robert Sheehan: *Metals*, Idaho, 99
Joel Shepard: *Wood*, Washington, 141
John Sheriff: *Wood*, New Mexico, 142
Carol Shinn: *Textiles*, Arizona, 123
David Simon: *Wood*, Oregon, 143
Susan Singleton: *Textiles*, Washington, 124
Kay Slusarenko: *Miscellaneous (Painted Murals)*, Oregon, 105
Paolo Soleri: *Metals*, Arizona, 100
Anne Storrs: *Ceramics*, Oregon, 59
Michael Strong: *Wood*, Washington, 144
Janet Taylor: *Textiles*, Arizona, 125
Terry Talty: *Metals*, Colorado, 101
Laurie Thal: *Glass*, Wyoming, 72
William Toney: *Wood*, Oregon, 143
Randy Turner: *Wood*, Washington, 145
M. Robert Van Arsdale: *Wood*, New Mexico, 10*
Anne Veraldi: *Ceramics*, Washington, 60
Charlene Vogel: *Textiles*, Oregon, 126
Paul Von Rosenstiel: *Lighting, Wood*, Washington, 81, 146
Steve Voorheis: *Wood*, Montana, 147
Bruce West: *Metals*, Oregon, 30, 102
Walter A. White: *Metals*, Washington, 32, 103
Judith Williams: *Ceramics*, Colorado, 61
Ken Williams: *Masonry & Concrete*, Colorado, 37, 88
Jay Wilson: *Wood*, Washington, 15*
Timothy Zikratch: *Lighting*, Idaho, 82

*Craftsmen not included in the catalog but whose work appears in the book

Harold Balazs
Route 2, Box 208
Mead, Washington 99021
509-466-3831

Philipp Baldwin
% Oregon School of Arts and Crafts
8245 S.W. Barnes Road
Portland, Oregon 97225
503-297-5544

Tim Girvin
Tim Girvin Design
911 Western Avenue
Suite 420
Seattle, Washington 98104
206-623-7808

Lu Himes
2316 N.W. Quimby
Portland, Oregon 97210
503-225-0336

J. Carl Freedman
Box 553
Cannon Beach, Oregon 97110
503-436-2922

Don Lelooska
5618 Lewis River Road
Ariel, Washington 98603
206-225-9522

Tim O'Neil
Inverness Glassworks
Route 2, Box 1127A
Troutdale, Oregon 97060
503-666-5223

M. Robert Van Arsdale
Heart Wood Custom Furniture
P.O. Box 333
San Cristobal, New Mexico 87564
505-776-2389

Jay Wilson
No address available

Index

This cross-referenced index is designed to give the reader an idea of the wide variety of objects that craftsmen can produce. It is composed of what is photographically represented in the book as well as other objects created by the craftsmen.